OXFORD

GCSE Maths for OCR

SPECIFICATION A

Revision Guide

Steve Cavill
Geoff Gibb
Jayne Kranat
Neil Tully

OCR
RECOGNISING ACHIEVEMENT

OXFORD
UNIVERSITY PRESS

Official Publisher Partnership

Great Clarendon Street, Oxford OX2 6DP

Oxford University Press is a department of the University of Oxford.

It furthers the University's objective of excellence in research, scholarship,
and education by publishing worldwide in

Oxford   New York

Auckland   Cape Town   Dar es Salaam   Hong Kong   Karachi
Kuala Lumpur   Madrid   Melbourne   Mexico City   Nairobi
New Delhi   Shanghai   Taipei   Toronto

With offices in

Argentina   Austria   Brazil   Chile   Czech Republic   France   Greece
Guatemala   Hungary   Italy   Japan   Poland   Portugal   Singapore
South Korea   Switzerland   Thailand   Turkey   Ukraine   Vietnam

British Library Cataloguing in Publication Data

Data available

ISBN: 978-0-19-912805-1
10 9 8 7 6 5 4 3

Printed in Great Britain by Bell and Bain Ltd, Glasgow

We are grateful to the following for permission to reproduce copyright material:

Front cover: Cathy Keifer/iStockphoto.com; zxcynosure/iStockphoto.com;
Oscar E. Gutierrez/iStockphoto.com; nel4/iStock

Paper used in the production of this book is a natural, recyclable product made
from wood grown in sustainable forests. The manufacturing process conforms to
the environmental regulations to the country of origin.

About this book

Produced in partnership with OCR, this revision guide contains
all the material you need to help you prepare for your Higher tier
examinations in OCR's GCSE in Mathematics A (J562). Written by
senior examiners and OCR teachers, the book provides:

- Key points, worked examples and exercises for each topic to help
  you fully consolidate the learning objectives
- Sample papers for valuable exam practice including the new
  assessment objectives
- A free CD-ROM containing all pages in PDF format for flexible
  learning, as well as full solutions and mark schemes for the
  sample papers

Contents

UNIT A

AN1	Arithmetic	2
AN2	Rounding and approximation	4
AN3	Calculator skills	6
AN4	Order of operations	8
AN5	Factors, multiples and primes	10
AN6	Basic ratio	12
AN7	Using ratio	14
AA1	Symbols	16
AA2	Brackets	18
AA3	Coordinates	19
AA4	Formulae	20
AA5	Sequences	22
AA6	Linear equations	24
AG1	The metric and imperial system	26
AG2	Constructions	28
AG3	Loci	30
AG4	Maps and bearings	32
AG5	Pythagoras' theorem	34
AG6	Core trigonometry	36
AS1	Collecting data	38
AS2	Averages	40
AS3	Comparing data	42
AS4	Box plots and cumulative frequency graphs	44
AS5	Histograms	46

UNIT B

BN1	Arithmetic with integers and decimals	48
BN2	Rounding and estimation	50
BN3	Calculating with fractions	52
BN4	Terminating and recurring decimals	54
BN5	Fractions and decimals	56
BN6	Percentages, fractions and decimals	58
BN7	Squares and cubes	60
BN8	Indices and index laws	62
BN9	Fractional indices and surds	64
BA1	Straight-line graphs	66
BA2	Real-life linear functions	68
BA3	Simultaneous equations	70
BA4	Inequalities	72
BG1	Angles, triangles and quadrilaterals	74
BG2	Polygons and quadrilaterals	76
BG3	Circle theorems	78
BG4	Symmetry, reflection and rotation	80
BG5	Translations and combining transformations	82
BG6	Similarity and congruence	84
BG7	Enlargements	86
BG8	Vectors and vector geometry	88
BS1	Scatter graphs	90
BS2	Time series	92

UNIT C

CN1	Calculating with fractions and rounding	94
CN2	Calculator display and accuracy	96
CN3	Calculator skills and formulae	98
CN4	Standard index form	100
CN5	Percentage problems	102
CN6	Direct and indirect proportion	104
CN7	Compound measures	106
CN8	Exponential growth and decay	108
CA1	3D coordinates	110
CA2	Trial and improvement	111
CA3	Quadratic expressions	112
CA4	Algebraic fractions	114
CA5	Quadratic equations	116
CA6	Quadratic graphs	118
CA7	Simultaneous linear and quadratic equations	120
CA8	Real-life graphs	122
CA9	Non-linear graphs	124
CA10	Transformation of functions	126
CG1	Area and perimeter of compound shapes	128
CG2	Circumference and area of circles	130
CG3	Surface area and volume	132
CG4	Length, area and volume scale factors	134
CG5	Sine and cosine rules	136
CG6	3D trigonometry	138
CS1	Theoretical probability	140
CS2	Listing outcomes and independent events	142
CS3	Experiments and relative frequency	144
CS4	Tree diagrams and independent events	146
	GCSE formulae	148
	Practice paper A	149
	Practice paper B	152
	Practice paper C	156
	Answers	161

- An **integer** is a whole number.

- When you multiply or divide an integer by 10, 100, 1000 … the digits do not change, only the number of zeros.

- When you **multiply**, move the digits **left** the same number of columns as there are **zeros** in the multiplier.

EXAMPLE

a $90 \times 100 = 9000$ **b** $2.9 \times 100 = 290$

a

←		9	0
9	0	0	0

b

←		2	.	9
2	9	0	.	

- When you **divide**, move the digits **right** the same number of columns as there are zeros in the divider.

EXAMPLE

a $41\,600 \div 100 = 416$ **b** $0.3 \div 10 = 0.03$

a

4	1	6	0	0
	→	4	1	6

b

0	.	3	→
0	.	0	3

Learn the rules for multiplying and dividing with **directed** (negative and positive) numbers.

× or ÷	−	+
−	+	−
+	−	+

Examples

a $2 \times -3 = -6$
b $-15 \div -3 = 5$
c $15 \times -2 \div 5 = -6$

EXAMINER'S TIP

As a check, count the number of minus signs.

If this is even, the answer is +

If it's odd, the answer is −

a only 1 minus (odd) answer −

b 2 minuses (even) answer +

c only 1 minus (odd) answer −

EXAMPLE

Sue, Liam and Jack share the cost of a meal equally.
The meal costs £24.60.
How much do they each pay?

$£24.60 \div 3 = £8.20$

Your calculator shows 8.2
Remember to put in the 0 and £ sign.

Learn the rules for multiplying and dividing by a positive number between 0 and 1.

×	The answer is smaller than the original number	$25 \times 0.5 = 12.5$	25 halves make 12.5
÷	The answer is bigger than the original number	$25 \div 0.5 = 50$	There are 50 halves in 25

Steve pays 15.27p a unit for his electricity.
He uses 418 units.
What is his bill, in pounds?

....

15.27p × 418 = 6382.86p
His bill is £63.83

Mia has a bag containing 2.4 kg of flour.
She has a recipe for 15 small cakes that uses 450 g of flour.
Mia makes 45 cakes. How many grams of flour are left in the bag?

....

   45 ÷ 15 = 3 (she makes 3 lots of cakes)
   3 × 450 g = 1350 g
2400 − 1350 = 1050 g
So 1050 g of flour are left in the bag.

The answer has to be in grams, so work in grams.

Exercise AN1

MEDIUM
LOW

1   Explain how you know these answers are wrong just by looking at them.
   a   123 × −2 = 246   **b**   25 ÷ −5 = 5   **c**   −8 × −5 × −2 = 80   **d**   10 × −2 = 20

2   Finn buys 24 large loaves to make sandwiches. Each loaf has 18 slices,
   including the end crusts, which he cannot use. He needs 2 slices to make a sandwich.
   How many sandwiches can he make?

3   Carla flies from London to Rome at Christmas. The temperature in
   Rome is 14 °C and the temperature in London is −5 °C.
   How much hotter is Rome than London?

4   Harry sees this Choc Star advert.
   a   How much money does he save if he buys 3 Choc Stars?
   b   Because they will melt quickly he sells one to Ali
      for 95p and one to Rita for 95p. How much has his
      Choc Star cost him?

Choc Star
£1.23 each or 3 for £2.80

5   This table shows the average heights, in mm, of boys and girls
   in the UK.
   a   How many mm do boys grow, on average, from the age of 11 years?
   b   How many mm does the average boy grow in height in 1 year?
   c   How many mm does the average girl grow in height in 1 year?
   d   Explain what your answers tell you and why
      this might not be the whole story.

6   Alan's car emits 0.11 kg of carbon every kilometre.
   How many kilometres has he driven if
   the car emits 1 tonne of carbon?

There are 1000 kg in 1 tonne.

		Height
Age	Girls	Boys
11	1440	1430
12	1500	1490
13	1550	1550
14	1590	1630
15	1610	1690
16	1620	1730
17	1620	1750
18	1620	1760

Rounding and approximation AN2

- The **decimal point** in a number comes between the **whole number** part and the **decimal fraction**.

| | | | | | | . | Decimal places | | |
Hundred thousands	Ten thousands	Thousands	Hundreds	Tens	Units	.	First	Second	Third
						.	Tenths	Hundredths	Thousandths
100 000	10 000	1000	100	10	1	.	$\frac{1}{10}$	$\frac{1}{100}$	$\frac{1}{1000}$
2	0	3	4	5	0	.	0	0	0

The number in the table is 'Two hundred and three thousand, four hundred and fifty'.

Significant means important.

If you start at the left-hand side of the number the first figure you come to that is **not 0** is the **first significant figure**.

> **EXAMPLE**
>
> Copy these numbers and underline the first significant figure.
> **a** 302 451.6   **b** 0.000 612   **c** 2.208   **d** 0.013 87
>
> ....
>
> **a** <u>3</u>02 451.6   **b** 0.000 <u>6</u>12   **c** <u>2</u>.208   **d** 0.0<u>1</u>3 87

Sometimes you have to round a number, for example, 'to the nearest 10' or 'to 1 significant figure (1 sf)' or 'to two decimal places' (2 dp).

To round a number

- Look at the digit after the one you have to round to.
- If that digit is 4 or less, replace it and all following digits with zeros.
  Write nothing more if you come to the decimal point.
- If that digit is 5 or more, add 1 to the figure before it and replace all following digits with zeros.
  Write nothing more if you come to the decimal point.

> **EXAMPLE**
>
> Round **a** 63.853   **b** 0.097 62
> **i** to 3 sf   **ii** to 2 sf   **iii** to 1 sf
>
> ....
>
> **a** **i** 63.853 = 63.9 to 3 sf   **ii** 63.853 = 64 to 2 sf   **iii** 63.853 = 60 to 1 sf
> **b** **i** 0.097 62 = 0.0976 to 3 sf   **ii** 0.097 62 = 0.098 to 2 sf   **iii** 0.097 62 = 0.1 to 1 sf

In part **b iii** the 9 is followed by a 7 so you must round up. When you round up 0.09 you get 0.1

Exercise AN2

MEDIUM

1   Write each of these numbers in words.
   a 11 384   b 2 010 345   c 45 000 20   d 23 444 012

2   Write each of these numbers in figures.
   a Twelve thousand, six hundred and nine
   b Fifty million, one hundred and twenty thousand and seven
   c One hundred and forty-two point two
   d Fifteen million, nine hundred and five thousand and fifty-three

3   Copy each number and underline the digit in the decimal place indicated.
   a 12.376 (second dp)   b 0.004 69 (first dp)   c 25.0936 (third dp)   d 3.5398 (second dp)

4   Round the numbers in question 3 correct to the decimal place indicated.

5   Copy each number and underline the first significant figure.
   a 12.376   b 0.004 69   c 25.0936   d 3.5398

6   Round each number as indicated.
   a 140 298 the nearest hundred
   b 34 718   1 sf
   c 0.580 76   1 dp
   d 17.099   1 dp
   e 45 970   1 sf
   f 1.973 04   2 dp
   g 2.619   1 sf
   h 0.002 84   1 sf
   i 825.774   2 dp
   j 16.99   1 dp

7   Calculate
   a 13×0.13 correct to 1 dp   b 4.56×4.56 correct to the nearest whole number
   c $1 \div 7$ correct to 2 dp   d $12.3 \div 1.6$ correct to 1 dp

8   Barry bought 16 litres of fuel at 119.9p a litre.
   How much did he pay for this fuel? (Round to the nearest penny.)

9   Chen buys 33 bags of potatoes at 86p a bag. He makes them into chips.
   Each bag of potatoes makes 7 portions of chips.
   a How much does Chen pay for the potatoes?
   b How many portions of chips does he make?
   c What is the cost of the potatoes per portion of chips? (Round to the nearest penny.)
   d How much should he charge for a portion of chips if he wants to make a profit of
      8p per portion?
   e How much profit does he make if he sells all the chips he makes?

You will need to practise with your own calculator as not all calculators have the same functions on their keys.

- The **square root** key is usually $\sqrt{}$

  If you have to **square root a whole calculation** then you may have to put brackets round the calculation.
  To find $\sqrt{64-21}$ you enter
  $\sqrt{}(64-21) =$ and the answer is 6.5574 ...

EXAMINER'S TIP

Without the brackets you may get −13, which is wrong. You may have to round the answer.

- The **cube root** key is usually $\sqrt[3]{}$

  Use this like the square root key.

- The **reciprocal** of a number is 1 ÷ the number. The key is x^{-1}

- If you have **a calculation written as a fraction**, put brackets round the top and bottom of the fraction and remember that a fraction is a division.

To find $\dfrac{23.4 - 6.27}{1.2 \times 2}$

write this as $\dfrac{(23.4 - 6.27)}{(1.2 \times 2)}$ and enter $(23.4 - 6.27) \div (1.2 \times 2) =$
The answer is 7.1375

EXAMPLE

Calculate the cost of one ticket if 15 tickets cost £18.

$18 \div 15 = 1.2 = £1.20$

EXAMINER'S TIP

Never write 1.2 for money, **always** £1.20

EXAMPLE

Bryony makes a solid cube by joining lots of 1 cm cubes together.
The cube is 6 cm along each edge. How many cubes has she used?

$6^3 = 216$ cubes

EXAMINER'S TIP

6^3 is tidier than $6 \times 6 \times 6$

Exercise AN3

1 Use your calculator to work out these calculations.
Round to 1dp if the answer is not exact.

  a 2.5^2

  b $\sqrt{625}$

  c $1.4^3 - 1.4^2$

  d $\sqrt[3]{1331}$

  e $\dfrac{(2.6 + 1.9)}{1.5}$

  f $\dfrac{4.6^2 - 2}{(5.1 + 2.3 - 3.4)}$

  g $\sqrt[3]{6.1^2 - 0.81}$

  h $\dfrac{\sqrt{2.5 \times 4}}{5^2}$

  i $\dfrac{4.5^3 + 1.3^2}{1.4 - 2}$

2 Calculate the **reciprocal** of these numbers.

  a 5

  b 0.2

  c 12

  d 100

  e 18

  f 0.08

What do you notice about the answers to **a** and **b**?

3 Darren buys 6 rolls of loft insulation.
Each roll is 5 m of insulation and is 400 mm wide.
He pays £77.94 for all six rolls.

  a What is the cost of 1 m of loft insulation?

  b How much does it cost to insulate 4 m² of the loft?

4 Here are some facts about metric lengths.
There are 1000 millimetres (mm) in 1 metre (m)
         100 centimetres (cm) in 1 metre
         1000 metres in 1 kilometre (km)

  a A shelf is 4.2 metres long. How many millimetres is this?

  b Paula walks 1.06 kilometres to school. How many
    metres is this?

  c A shelf is 140 mm wide. A shelf bracket is 0.1 m wide.
    Can the bracket be used to hold up the shelf?

  d The head teacher wants to take a picture of all the pupils
    lined up, shoulder to shoulder, along the school drive.
    There are 430 pupils in the school. The average width
    of a pupil across the shoulders is 380 mm. The drive is
    150 m long. Can the photograph be taken in a single line?

5 This formula can be used to change between miles and kilometres.

  distance in miles ⟶ $\times 1.6$ ⟶ distance in kilometres

  Change   **a** 14 miles into kilometres   **b** 32 kilometres into miles.

6 A bag contains 1.8 kilograms of sugar.
Gemma uses 560 grams of the sugar to make a cake and
196 g to fill her sugar bowl.
How much sugar is left in the bag?

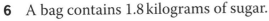

There are 1000 grams in 1 kilogram.

All scientific calculators use these rules BUT you still need to check your answers in case of error.

B	**B**rackets	Do any calculations in brackets first, using the BIDMAS order.
I	**I**ndices	Indices are **powers** like $\square^3$ or $\sqrt{\square}$
D	Divide	These are equal in importance
M	**M**ultiply	
A	**A**dd	These are equal in importance
S	**S**ubtract	

If all the signs are equal in importance, then work from left to right.

When a calculation is a fraction like $\dfrac{12 + 6}{5 - 3}$, put brackets in the calculator so $(12 + 6) \div (5 - 3) = 9$

Try it on your calculator, without brackets, and you will get 10.2 ✗

You may be given a calculation and asked to put brackets in to make the answer correct.

Write the calculation in the working space and try brackets in different places to get the answer.

Only write the brackets in the **answer space** when you have got it right.

Try $6 \times 5 - 1 + 3 = 27$ The answer to the calculation without using brackets is 32.
Try $6 \times 5 - (1 + 3)$ ✗   The answer is 26 ... **try it yourself.**
Try $6 \times (5 - 1) + 3$ ✓   This is right $(6 \times 4 + 3 = 27)$.

Calculate **a** $3.4 + 1.2 \times 5$ **b** $(5 - 1.2)^2$ **c** $\dfrac{(14.3 - 4^2)}{(5+3)}$

a $3.4 + 1.2 \times 5 = 3.4 + 6 = 9.4$

b $(5 - 1.2)^2 = 3.8^2 = 14.44$

c $\dfrac{-1.7}{(5+3)} = \dfrac{-1.7}{8} = -0.2125$ or -0.2 to 2dp

EXAMINER'S TIP

$5 - 1.2$ is in a bracket so is done first

EXAMINER'S TIP

When you enter this in your calculator, type

$(14.3 - 4$ $) \div (5 + 3)$

Exercise AN4

MEDIUM

1 Use your calculator to work out the following.

  a $2.1 + 5.8 \times 3$
  b $4.2 - 2.6 \div 2$
  c $(1 + 4.3) \times 3 - 6.1$
  d $4 - 2 \times (3.4 + 1.2)$
  e $3 - (2 \times 1.4 + 1)$
  f $12 + 2(3.3 \times 4) - 2$

2 Do a rough calculation to check the answers to question 1. Part **a** is done for you.

  a $2 + 6 \times 3$
    $= 2 + 18$
    $= 20$

3 Use your calculator to work out the following.
  Give the answer to 1dp where necessary.

  a $\dfrac{3 \times 5}{1 + 2}$
  b $\dfrac{(1.3 + 2 \times 3.7)}{1.3 + 0.2}$
  c $\dfrac{3 \times 5.2 - 4.5}{3.2 - 2}$

  d $\dfrac{(10.2 - 3.1 \times 2.4)}{2.2 + 1.6}$
  e $\dfrac{3^2 \times 5}{1 + 2^2}$
  f $\sqrt{(12.3 + 4.7)}$

  g $\dfrac{\sqrt{18.8 - 9.8} + 9.6}{1.2}$
  h $\dfrac{(6 + 8)^2}{2.5^2 - 1.5^2}$

4 Put brackets into each calculation to make the answer correct.

  a $1 + 2 \times 3 = 9$
  b $1 + 2 \times 3 - 4 = -1$
  c $10 - 3 + 2 \times 5 = -15$
  d $10 - 3 + 2 \times 5 = 45$
  e $10 - 3 + 2 \times 5 = -3$
  f $14 + 5 \times 2^2 = 76$
  g $14 + 5 \times 2^2 = 114$
  h $12 - 2 + 5 \times 2 + 1 = 1$

5 Clive the electrician charges a "call out" fee of £25 and then £15 for each half hour he works. Owen calls Clive to mend his immersion heater. The job takes 90 minutes.
  Owen works out what he thinks he will pay, like this:
  $(£25 + £15) \times 3 = £120$

  a Is Owen right?
  b What calculation should Owen have done?
  c What was Owen's real bill?

A **multiple** of a number is in its multiplication table.
$5, 10, 15, \ldots = 1 \times 5, 2 \times 5, 3 \times 5, \ldots$

- A **common multiple** of two (or more) numbers is a multiple of both numbers; for example, 28 is a common multiple of 4 and 7.

- A **least common multiple (LCM)** of two (or more) numbers is the lowest number that they both divide into; for example, the LCM of 4 and 7 is 28.

EXAMPLE

Find the LCM of 12 and 15.

Multiples of 12: 12, 24, 36, 48, **60**, 72, 84 …
Multiples of 15: 15, 30, 45, **60**, …
The LCM of 12 and 15 = 60

- A **factor** divides exactly into a number.
  1, 2, 3, 4 and 6 are all factors of 12.

Notice that 1 is not a prime number (it does not have two factors).

A **prime number** has **only** two factors, the number itself and 1.
Learn this list of the first ten prime numbers:

2, 3, 5, 7, 11, 13, 17, 19, 23, 29.

Test to see if a number is prime by dividing it by 2 then 3 then 5 … If you get a whole number at any point, the number is not prime.

A **prime factor** is a factor of a number that is also prime.
- 3 is a factor of 12 and it is prime so 3 is a prime factor of 12.
- You can write a number as the **product** of its prime factors, for example $24 = 2 \times 2 \times 2 \times 3 = 2^3 \times 3$

2 and 3 are prime factors of 12.

EXAMPLE

Write 60 as the product of its prime factors.

$60 = \mathbf{3} \times 20$
$20 = 4 \times \mathbf{5}$
$4 = \mathbf{2 \times 2}$ $\qquad 60 = 2 \times 2 \times 3 \times 5 = 2^2 \times 3 \times 5$

- The **highest common factor** is the largest number that divides into a pair or group of numbers.

Find the highest common factor (HCF) of 42 and 90.

First write each number as the product of prime factors.
42 = **2** × **3** × 7 and 90 = **2** × **3** × 3 × 5
The HCF of 42 and 90 = 2 × 3 = 6

Exercise AN5

 MEDIUM

1 Write the first five multiples of each number.
 a 6   b 8   c 17
 d 23   e 51   f 242

2 Find all the factors of each number.
 a 16   b 21   c 36
 d 43   e 120   f 552

3 Find all the prime numbers between 30 and 50.

4 Work out whether each number is prime or not. Show your working.
 a 27   b 83   c 123
 d 117   e 215   f 401

5 Write each number as the product of its prime factors.
 a 30   b 72   c 98
 d 130   e 166   f 1024

6 For each of the following, find the least common multiple.
 a 12 and 30   b 16 and 24   c 22 and 12
 d 6, 15 and 20 e 9, 12 and 15

7 Find the highest common factor of each set of numbers in question 6.

8 Two model cars start together at 9 o'clock on a track.
 One takes 10 seconds to complete the track and the other takes 12 seconds.
 At what time will they next pass each other on the starting line?

Factors, multiples and primes   11

A **ratio** compares the size of two or more amounts.

A family has 6 pet animals.
4 animals are dogs (D) and 2 animals are cats (C) so
D : C = 4 : 2.
There are twice as many dogs as cats, so the ratio can also be
written D : C = 2 : 1.

> If A = 1 kg and B = 500 g A : B is not 1 : 500.
> Change A to 1000 g and A : B = 1000 : 500.
> (This means that A is twice as big as B.)

- Amounts must be in the same units to write a ratio.

- A ratio does not have any units because it compares
  relative amounts.

EXAMINER'S TIP

A : B = 3 kg : 2 kg ✗
But A : B = 3 : 2 ✓

A : B = 3 : 2 means that, for every two "shares" of B there are
three "shares" of A.

So, A is $1\frac{1}{2}$ times as big as B ($3 = 2 \times 1\frac{1}{2}$).

Here are five ways you can change a ratio.

1 **Simplify** the ratio by dividing each "share" by a common
   factor.

$12 : 4 = 3 : 1 (\div 4)$

2 Multiply each "share" by the same number.

$2 : 1 = 6 : 3 (\times 3)$

3 Write the ratio in the form **1 : _n_**.
   Divide all the "shares" by the "share" that is to become 1.

$6 : 27 = 1 : 4.5 (\div 6)$

4 Change the ratio to a fraction by writing one "share"
   as a fraction of the whole amount (all the "shares").

$3 : 4 \qquad 3 + 4 = 7$
$\frac{3}{7} \qquad \left(\text{or } \frac{4}{7} \right)$

5 Change the ratio to a fraction by writing one "share"
   as a fraction of another "share".
   o The one "share" is the numerator.
   o Write the second "share" as the denominator.

$3 : 4$
$\frac{3}{4} \qquad \left(\text{or } \frac{4}{3} \right)$

> Divide by 2.
> This is like cancelling fractions.
> Always check that there are no more
> common factors to divide by.

EXAMPLE

a Simplify F : G : H = 4 : 6 : 10
b Simplify H : J = 1.4 : 0.9
c Write P : Q = 4 : 5 in the form 1 : _n_.

> Multiply by 10 so there are no decimals.

a F : G : H = 2 : 3 : 5
b H : J = 14 : 9
c P : Q = 1 : 1.25

> P has to be 1, so divide both "shares"
> by 4.

Sue, Terry and Unity are left some money.
They divide it between them in the ratio
S : T : U = 2 : 3 : 5

a   What fraction does Sue have of the whole amount?

b   What fraction is Sue's "share" of Unity's share?

a   There are 2 + 3 + 5 = 10 "shares"

Sue has $\frac{2}{10}$ or $\frac{1}{5}$ of all the "shares".

b   Sue has 2 "shares" and Unity has 5.

Sue has $\frac{2}{5}$ of Unity's "share".

2 and 5 have no common factors so cannot be cancelled.

Exercise AN6

MEDIUM

1   Write each ratio as simply as possible, using only whole numbers.

   a   P : Q = 10 : 15   b   G : M = 12 : 9
   c   R : P = 24 : 36   d   K : J = 3.6 : 1.2
   e   A : B : C = 20 : 30 : 40   f   A : G : P = 45 : 18 : 54
   g   R : U : F = 2.4 : 0.6 : 1.8   h   J : K = 1.5 : 2
   i   S : H : G = 12 : 1.5 : 4   j   P : S = 5 : 0.5

2   Write each ratio in the form 1 : n.

   a   S : T = 3 : 12   b   G : H = 10 : 5   c   F : K = 1.2 : 1.8
   d   J : G = 240 : 600   e   L : K = 9 : 1.8   f   P : M = 20 : 4.4

3   Write each ratio in the form n : 1.

   a   K : P = 25 : 20   b   H : S = 1 : 2.5   c   G : Y = 24 : 19.2
   d   B : G = 14.2 : 8.52 e   S : Y = 3 : 0.5   f   M : T = 4.2 : 4.8

4   In each case write the ratio A : B, giving your answer in its simplest form.

   a   A = 5 kg   B = 12 kg   b   A = 5 kg   B = 1500 g   c   A = 12 minutes   B = 1 hour
   d   A = £10   B = 50p   e   A = 3 days   B = 3 weeks   f   A = 25 cm   B = 1.2 m

5   In each case write the ratio A : B : C, giving your answer in its simplest form.

   a   A = £2   B = 75p   C = £1.50   b   A = 4 litres   B = 6 litres   C = 500 millilitres
   c   A = 10 cm   B = 0.2 m   C = 1 m   d   A = 40 mm   B = 2 cm   C = 1 m
   e   A = £24   B = 5p   C = £5.50   f   A = 5 hours   B = 20 minutes   C = $1\frac{1}{2}$ hours

6   a   S : R = 2 : 5. What fraction is S of R?

   b   G : K : P = 1 : 3 : 4. What fraction is P of the total?

   c   M : V = 9 : 5. What fraction is V of M?

   d   A : H : Y = 3 : 2 : 6. What fraction is A of Y?

   e   G : H : T = 1 : 2 : 5. What fraction is H of T?

   f   P : G : X = 4 : 6 : 5. What fraction is P of the total?

Using ratio

You can use ratios to find the solutions to problems.

To divide an amount in a ratio
- Add up all the "shares" of the ratio.
- Divide the amount by the total number of shares.
- Multiply each share by the given ratio.

Share £2000 in the ratio 2 : 3.

$2 + 3 = 5$

£2000 ÷ 5 = £400

£400 × 3 = £1200

£400 × 2 = £800

EXAMPLE

Divide 2.4 kg in the ratio M : N = 3 : 5.

$3 + 5 = 8$ (Add all the shares)

2.4 kg ÷ 8 = 0.3 kg (Find the value of 1 share)

M = 3 × 0.3 kg = 0.9 kg and

N = 5 × 0.3 kg = 1.5 kg

> **EXAMINER'S TIP**
>
> Check that all the weights add up to the whole amount (2.4 kg).
> (0.9 + 1.5 = 2.4 ✓)

To find the total amount when you know one share
- Add up all the "shares"
- Divide the known value by the size of its "share"
- Multiply these two amounts together.

You can also find the size of each of the other shares. After the second step, just multiply the value of one "share" by the size of each other "share".

> **EXAMINER'S TIP**
>
> This could be where ingredients are mixed in a ratio. You will know the weight of one of the ingredients and the ratio. You have to find the weight of the other ingredients.

EXAMPLE

Peter uses his phone to make texts and calls.

The ratio of the number of calls to the number of texts is 7 : 5.

He sends 140 texts. How many calls does he make?

1 share = 140 ÷ 5 = 28 (Find the value of 1 share)

Number of calls = 28 × **7** = 196 (Calls have **7** shares)

EXAMPLE

A recipe uses flour, sugar and butter in the ratio 5 : 3 : 2 by weight. 75 g of sugar is used.

a What weight of each ingredient is used?

b What is the total weight of the mixture?

a 1 share = 75 g ÷ 3 = 25 g (Find the value of 1 share)

Amount of flour 5 × 25 g = 125 g (Flour has **5** shares)

Amount of butter 2 × 25 g = 50 g (Butter has **2** shares)

b Total weight = 25 g × (5 + 3 + 2) = 25 g × 10 = 250 g

> **EXAMINER'S TIP:**
>
> Check that total weight = Sum of shares
>
> 250g = 75g + 125g + 50g.
> 25g × (5 + 3 + 2) = 250g ✓

Exercise AN7

MEDIUM

1 In each case, divide the amount in the ratio given.
  a   £25 in the ratio A : B = 1 : 4   **b**   200 g in the ratio A : B = 7 : 3
  c   2.8 kg in the ratio A : B = 3 : 5   **d**   3 hours in the ratio A : B : C = 5 : 3 : 1

2 **a**   Find the total amount when A = 4.5 kg and A : B = 5 : 4.
   b   Find G when A = £6.40 and A : G = 5 : 8.
   c   Find P when S = 30p and P : S = 12 : 5.
   d   Find W and X when Z = 4 litres and W : X : Z = 1 : 15 : 8.

3 John and Andrew take part in a sponsored walk.
  a   The amounts they raise are in the ratio John : Andrew = 4 : 5.
     John raises £48.60.
      i   How much does Andrew raise?   **ii**   How much do they raise altogether?
  b   The amount they raise is $\frac{3}{40}$ of the total amount raised. How much is raised altogether?

4 Paula's garden is divided into lawn (L), flowers (F), paths (P) and vegetables (V)
   in the ratio L : F : P : V = 10 : 6 : 3 : 8. The area of the lawn is 45 m².
  a   What area is planted with vegetables?
  b   What fraction of the garden is flowers?

5 A wholemeal biscuit weighs 12.5 g and contains the nutrients listed in the table.
  a   What is the weight of the "Other" nutrients?
  b   What is the ratio of carbohydrate to fat?
  c   What is the ratio of fat : fibre?
  d   Explain what your answer to part **c** tells you about the
     amounts of fat : fibre in these biscuits.

Carbohydrate	7.0 g
Fat	1.2 g
Fibre	1.8 g
Other	2.5 g

  e   The maker of the biscuits claims, "Less than $\frac{1}{10}$ of our biscuit
     is fat". Is this true? Explain your answer.

6 Connor uses his car for work (W) and pleasure (P). The ratio of the miles
   he drives is W : P = 4 : 3. One month he drives 1470 miles.
  a   How many miles does he drive for pleasure during that month?
   Connor spends £160.80 buying fuel for all his driving that month.
   He claims 40p a mile from his company for the miles that he drives for work.
  b   Does the money he claims cover the cost of the petrol he buys?

7 Shades of pink paint can be made by mixing white (W)
   and red (R) paint in these ratios by volume.
   The more white is used, the paler the colour.
  a   Which ratio makes the darkest pink?
  b   If Gretta wants 3 litres of "Sunset", what volume of
     red and what volume of white paint will she need to mix?

Name	Ratio W : R
Sunset	5 : 3
Rose	5 : 2
Pale	6 : 1
Hint	25 : 3

  c   Alan mixes 1.2 litres of white with 200 ml of red. Which shade has he made?
  d   Karen wants to mix "Hint" and has 600 ml of red . If she uses all of this, with
     the correct amount of white to make the paint, what volume of "Hint" has she made?

Symbols

- In **equations** a letter represents a specific unknown number to be found. For example $5x = 20$

  > An equation is true for some values of x, an identity is true for all values of x.

- An **identity** is true for all values of the letters used and is used when writing expressions more simply. For example, $x + x \equiv 2x$

  > Technically an identity should be written with the identity symbol $\equiv$ rather than the equals sign $=$.

- A **formula** is used when we need to substitute different values of a variable. For example, $A = \pi r^2 h$

  > r and h are the variables.

- **Expressions** can be simplified by **collecting like terms** or using powers. For example, $2x + x$ simplifies to $3x$

EXAMPLE

Simplify

a $r \times r \times r \times r \times r$ **b** $6p + 5r + 3p - 4r$ **c** $\dfrac{15ab}{5b}$

a $r \times r \times r \times r \times r$ **b** $6p + 5r + 3p - 4r$ **c** $\dfrac{15ab}{5b} = \dfrac{3ab}{b}$

$= r^5$ $= 6p + 3p + 5r - 4r$ $= 3a$

                $= 9p + r$

EXAMPLE

Decide whether the following are equations, identities or formulae.

$3m + 6 + m + 11 = 4m + 17$ $3m + 6 = 18$

$v = u + at$ $\dfrac{r}{2} = r + 2$

> A question like this may or may not use the identity symbol ($\equiv$).

$3m + 6 + m + 11 = 4m + 17$ is an identity as it is true for all values of m.

$v = u + at$ is a formula

$3m + 6 = 18$ and $\dfrac{r}{2} = r + 2$ are both equations and are only true when $m = 4$ and $r = -4$ respectively.

EXAMPLE

Evaluate these expressions.

a $3x - 5$ when $x = 2$ **b** $2x^2 + 3$ when $x = -3$

a $3 \times 2 - 5 = 6 - 5$ **b** $2 \times (-3)^2 + 3 = 2 \times 9 + 3$

              $= 1$ $= 18 + 3$

                                        $= 21$

Exercise AA1

1 Simplify

  a $y + 6y + 2y - 5y$ **b** $c \times c \times c \times c$ **c** $s + 5t + 7s - 8t$

  d $4 \times z \times z \times 3 \times z$ **e** $4g - 2h - 5g - 7h$ **f** $6q + r - 5q - 5r + 4r - q$

2 Decide whether the following are equations, expressions, identities or formulae.

  a $8 - 2f = 10$ **b** $2(r - 5) = 2r - 10$ **c** $A = 4\pi r^2$

  d $v^2 = u^2 + 2as$ **e** $y = 8y + 21$ **f** $6r \times 4 = 8 \times (2r + r)$

3 Evaluate these expressions, given that $x = 6$.

  a $3x + 2$ **b** $10 - x$ **c** x^2

  d $\dfrac{10x - 16}{2}$ **e** $3x^2$

4 Simplify these expressions by collecting like terms.

  a $3a + 4b + 8a + 2b$ **b** $3t + 9 - t + 17$

  c $3x - 4y - 2x - 8y$ **d** $9p + p^2 + 5p$

  e $10xy + 10yx$ **f** $6ab + 2ba - ba$

5 Three students tried to simplify $3m + 5$. Which of them did it correctly?

  $3m + 5 = 8m$ $3m + 5 = 15m$ $3m + 5 = 3m + 5$

6 Simplify these expressions.

  a $4m \times 7n$ **b** $6m \times 2m$ **c** $\dfrac{20p}{2}$ **d** $\dfrac{14p}{7a}$

  e $2a \times 3b \times 4c$ **f** $k \times 2k \times 3k$ **g** $\dfrac{20ab}{5a}$ **h** $\dfrac{45c^2}{5c}$

7 Simplify the expressions in the grid and find the 'odd one out' for each row.

$3p + 2q + p + 5q$	$6p + 3q - 2p + 4q$	$5p - 3q - p + 5q$
$2m \times 3n$	$2 \times n \times m \times 5$	$6mn$
$\dfrac{24cd}{12c}$	$\dfrac{2d^2}{d^2}$	$\dfrac{2d^2}{d}$
$2n - 8$	$3m + 2n - m - 2m$	$3n - 2 - 6 - n$

8 a Write a simplified expression for the

    i perimeter   **ii** area of this rectangle

$4p$

8

  b What are the measurements of a rectangle with perimeter $6x + 4y$ and area $6xy$?

UNIT A

Brackets

AA2

You can **expand** (multiply out) brackets by multiplying every term inside the bracket by the term outside, for example

$$5(x + 2) = 5x + 10$$

EXAMPLE

Expand

a $4(x - 6)$ **b** $r(r + 2)$ **c** $a(a + b - 3c)$

Remember to multiply every term inside the bracket by the term outside.

a $4(x - 6) = 4x - 24$ **b** $r(r + 2) = r^2 + 2r$
c $a(a + b - 3c) = a^2 + ab - 3ac$

r^2 means $r \times r$.

You can **factorise** an expression by putting it in brackets with the **highest common factor** outside (the opposite of multiplying out), for example

$$9y - 6 = 3(3y - 2)$$

Find the HCF of each of the terms (in this case 3).

EXAMPLE

Factorise

a $3c - 12$ **b** $36 - 24k$ **c** $2m^2 + 8m$

a • Look for a number (or letter) that is a factor of each term – in this case 3.
 • Write the 3, then a set of brackets – like this $3(\ldots - \ldots)$.
 • In the spaces, write in the numbers or letters which give the original expression when the brackets are expanded – in this case $3(c - 4)$

Check your answer by expanding.
$3(c - 4) = 3c - 12$

b $36 - 24k = 12(3 - 2k)$

Choose the largest factor, in this case 12.

c Here, both 2 and m are factors, so
 $2m^2 + 8m = 2m(m + 4)$

Exercise AA2

MEDIUM

1 Expand these expressions.
  a $4(c + 5)$ **b** $7(y + 7)$ **c** $p(p - 7)$
  d $y(y + z)$ **e** $2e(e + 5f)$ **f** $3f(3f - h + 5h)$

2 Factorise.
  a $5h - 20$ **b** $28 + 7k$ **c** $f^2 + 9f$
  d $4j + 12$ **e** $18d - 24$ **f** $40 - 60m$
  g $pq - q^2$ **h** $3g^2 + 6g$ **i** $8mn + 12n^2$

EXAMINER'S TIP

If there are 2 factors the question will normally be worth 2 marks.

Coordinates

- You use **coordinates** to specify the position of a point on a grid.
- The **midpoint** of a **line segment** is halfway between its ends.
- You can calculate the length using **Pythagoras' theorem**.

You can revise Pythagoras' theorem. on page 34.

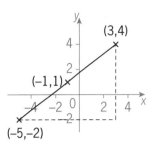

UNIT A

EXAMPLE

Point A is at $(-2, 1)$, point B is at $(6, 4)$.

a Find the midpoint of the line AB.

b Calculate the length of line AB.

> Technically AB should be called a **line segment**, as a line is infinitely long.

Start by drawing a sketch.

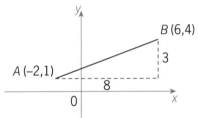

> You can think of the midpoint as the 'mean average' point.

a The midpoint is at $\left(\dfrac{-2 + 6}{2}, \dfrac{1 + 4}{2} \right) = (2, 2.5)$

b By Pythagoras:

$$c^2 = a^2 + b^2$$
$$c^2 = 8^2 + 3^2$$
$$= 64 + 9$$
$$= 73$$
$$c = \sqrt{73} = 8.54 \text{ units}$$

> **LOOK FORWARD** ➔
> See topic AG5 to revise Pythagoras' theorem.

> $\sqrt{73}$ is an 'exact' answer.
> 8.54 is correct to 3 significant figures

Exercise AA3

MEDIUM HIGH

1 For each of these pairs of points, A and B,

   i find the midpoint of AB

   ii find the length of AB. Give your answer to 3 significant figures where appropriate.

    a A(1, 1) B(4, 5)   **b** A(1, 4) B(7, 0)   **c** A(−1, −4) B(6, 2)

    d A(2, −3) B(−4, −1)   **e** A(−5, −2) B(3, 13)   **f** A(0, −2) B(7, 0)

2 PQRS is a rectangle.

   P, Q and R are the points $(-1, -2)$, $(1, 4)$ and $(7, 2)$ respectively.

   a Find the coordinates of point S.

   M is the midpoint of PQ and N is the midpoint of QR.

   b Show that the length of MN is exactly $\sqrt{20}$.

Formulae

- A **formula** is used to work out unknown values from known values. This is called **substituting**.

If $y = x^2 - 10$, find y when $x = 5$

$y = 5^2 - 10$
$\quad = 25 - 10$
$\quad = 15$

You can **derive** a formula using information you know.
For example, the area of a square of side t is given by $A = t^2$.

If $s = ut + \frac{1}{2}at^2$, find s when $u = 4$, $t = 5$ and $a = -2$.

$s = ut + \frac{1}{2}at^2$

$\quad = 4 \times 5 + \frac{1}{2} \times -2 \times 5^2$

$\quad = 20 - 25$

$\quad = -5$

Find and simplify a formula for the mean average, M, of the values, $3f$, $4f$, $9f$ and $12g$.

Mean, $M = \dfrac{3f + 4f + 9f + 12g}{4}$

$M = \dfrac{16f + 12g}{4}$

$M = 4f + 3g$

You can revise the mean average on page 40.

You can **rearrange** or **change the subject** of a formula by applying the same operation to each side.

The letter on its own on one side is called the **subject** of the formula.

Rearrange these formulae to make p the subject.

r is the subject of this formula because the formula begins $r =$

a $r = 3p + q$ **b** $t = p^2 - w$ **c** $u(p + r) = 6w + z$

a $\quad r = 3p + q$

$\quad r - q = 3p \quad$ subtract q from both sides

$\quad p = \dfrac{r - q}{3} \quad$ divide both sides by 3

b $\quad t = p^2 - w$

$\quad t + w = p^2 \quad$ add w to both sides

$\quad p = \sqrt{t + w} \quad$ take the square root of both sides

Technically it should be

c $\quad u(p + r) = 6w + z$

$\quad up + ur = 6w + z \quad$ expand the brackets

$\quad up = 6w + z - ur \quad$ subtract ur from each side

$\quad p = \dfrac{6w + z - ur}{u} \quad$ divide both sides by u

Compare the operations used here to those used in solving equations. The processes are very similar but tend to be used on letters in rearranging formulae and numbers in solving equations.

Rearrange this formula to make d the subject.

$3d + e = f - gd$

$3d + e = f - gd$

$3d + gd + e = f$ Collect the terms in d on one side ...

$3d + gd = f - e$ ... and any other terms on the other side

$d(3 + g) = f - e$ Factorise

$d = \dfrac{f - e}{3 + g}$ Divide both sides by $3 + g$

If the letter you are trying to make the subject appears on both sides, you collect any terms it appears in on one side and then **factorise**.

Exercise AA4

MEDIUM HIGH

1 If $p = 6$, $q = -2$ and $r = 3$, find the value of w if

  a $w = 8q - 5$ **b** $w = pq + qr$ **c** $w = pqr^2$

  d $w = \sqrt{pq^2 r}$ **e** $w = \dfrac{p(q + r)}{12}$ **f** $w = \sqrt[3]{(pr)^2 + 11q^2}$

2 **a**   A window cleaner charges £p for each window she cleans plus an extra £4. Write down a formula for the amount she charges, £C, for cleaning w windows.

    b   Write down a formula for the shaded area.

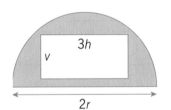

3 Rearrange these formulae to make x the subject.

  a $y = mx + c$ **b** $t = wx - g$ **c** $s = ab + rx$ **d** $q = r(x - z)$

  e $f = 3m - x$ **f** $p = \dfrac{y}{x}$ **g** $c = \dfrac{x}{t} - d$ **h** $k(x + w) = 5w - 7$

  i $x^2 y = z$ **j** $\dfrac{x^2 + a}{c} = d$ **k** $r = \sqrt{a + x}$ **l** $m = \sqrt{ax + b}$

4 Rearrange these formulae to make t the subject.

  a $3t = mt + d$ **b** $rt + f = 7 - 2t$ **c** $3p + 6t - m = m + dt$ **d** $t = r(t - s)$

  e $t(m - 5) = a(12 - t)$ **f** $3(t + 1) + 2(t - 6) = g(t + 5)$ **g** $\dfrac{pt}{t + 1} = 3$ **h** $4(t - k) = \dfrac{kt}{3}$

5 **a**   The area of an ellipse is given by the formula $A = \pi ab$ where a and b are the lengths shown in the diagram. Rearrange $A = \pi ab$ to make a the subject.

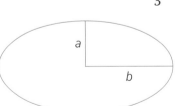

    b   A machine cuts ellipses out of a rectangular sheet of metal, 40 cm by 50 cm, to make cases for thermometers. The ellipses have $a = 3$ cm and $b = 5$ cm. The axes of symmetry of the ellipses have to be parallel to the edges of the sheet of metal.

    Calculate how much more area of metal is wasted if the ellipses are cut with b parallel to the 50 cm side rather than the 40 cm side. Explain why this calculation may not be accurate in real life.

A **sequence** has a **term-to-term** rule or a **position-to-term** rule.

You can generate a sequence with an nth term by putting $n = 1, 2, 3, \ldots$ and so on in the position-to-term rule.
The first three terms of the sequence whose nth term is $n^2 + 3$ are $1^2 + 3 = 4$, $2^2 + 3 = 7$, $3^2 + 3 = 12$.

In a **linear sequence** you add the same number each time to get the next term, for example

$7, 11, 15, 19, \ldots$ and $26, 24, 22, 20, \ldots$ are linear sequences.

> You can add a positive or a negative number.

You can find the **nth term** (the position-to-term rule) of a linear sequence by looking at the differences between the terms.
The nth term of the sequence $7, 11, 15, 19, \ldots$ is $4n + 3$

You should be familiar with these sequences.

Odd and even numbers	Squares $1, 4, 9, 16, \ldots$	Cubes $1, 8, 27, 64, \ldots$
Triangle numbers $1, 3, 6, 10, 15, \ldots$	Fibonacci numbers $1, 1, 2, 3, 5, 8, 13, \ldots$	Primes $2, 3, 5, 7, 11, \ldots$

> 1 is not a prime number.

EXAMPLE

Calculate the first term and the tenth term of the sequences with these nth terms.

a $3n - 2$ **b** $6 - n^2$ **c** $2^n - 1$

a first term $= 3 \times 1 - 2$ tenth term $= 3 \times 10 - 2$
$\qquad\qquad\quad = 1$ $= 30 - 2$
$\qquad\qquad\qquad\qquad\qquad\qquad\qquad\qquad\quad = 28$

b first term $= 6 - 1^2$ tenth term $= 6 - 10^2$
$\qquad\qquad\quad = 6 - 1$ $= 6 - 100$
$\qquad\qquad\quad = 5$ $= -94$

c first term $= 2^1 - 1$ tenth term $= 2^{10} - 1$
$\qquad\qquad\quad = 2 - 1$ $= 1024 - 1$
$\qquad\qquad\quad = 1$ $= 1023$

Find the nth term of the sequence with first five terms   11, 17, 23, 29, 35, …

Look at the differences between the terms.

The sequence goes up in 6s so the nth term starts $6n$.

Look at the first few terms of the sequence with nth term $6n$, that is, 6, 12, 18, …

The terms you want are all 5 more than these.

So the nth term is $6n + 5$

11   17   23
+6   +6

EXAMINER'S TIP

Don't just write '+6' on the answer line – that will score nothing.

Exercise AA5

MEDIUM

1   Write down the first two terms of the sequences with these nth terms.

   a $5n + 11$ **b** $7n + 1$ **c** $10n$ **d** $0.2n + 1.4$

   e $12 - 2n$ **f** $40 - 20n$ **g** $n^2 + n$ **h** $n^3 - n^n$

2   Find the eighth term of the sequences with these nth terms.

   a $12n - 9$ **b** $8 - n$

3   **a** Draw the next L shape in this pattern.

   b Copy and complete this table to show the number of shaded squares.

Pattern	1	2	3	4
Number of squares	3	5		

Pattern 1 Pattern 2   Pattern 3

   c How many squares will be shaded in Pattern 100?

4   Find a formula for the number of lines in a pattern like these with n hexagons.

1 hexagon

2 hexagons

3 hexagons

5   Marcus is adding 10 g weights to a spring. He measures the length of the spring after he has added each weight. Here are his results.

Number of 10 g weights added	1	2	3	4
Length of spring (cm)	38	41.5	45	48.5

   a Explain how Marcus can tell that there is a linear relationship between the number of weights and the length of the spring.

   b Find a formula for the length of the spring when n weights have been added.

   c How many weights must Marcus add to make the spring 1 metre long?

6   A sequence has nth term $7n + k$ where k is an integer between −5 and 5.

   The eighth term is a 2-digit Fibonacci number with two identical digits.

   The fourth term is a cube number.

   Find k and hence find the first term of the sequence that is a prime number.

You **solve** an **equation** by finding the value of an unknown quantity.

For example if $3x + 1 = 10$ the value of x is 3.

You do the same operation to each side of the equation so that it still balances.

Full working:
$3x + 1 = 10$
$3x = 9$ Subtract 1 from each side
$x = 3$ Divide both sides by 3
The **solution** is $x = 3$

EXAMPLE

Solve   **a** $5x + 6 = 2x - 9$ **b** $\dfrac{6m+7}{2} = 5$

a $5x + 6 = 2x - 9$
$3x + 6 = -9$ Subtract $2x$ from both sides
$3x = -15$ Subtract 6 from both sides
$x = -5$ Divide both sides by 3

b $\dfrac{6m+7}{2} = 5$
$6m + 7 = 10$ Multiply both sides by 2
$6m = 3$ Subtract 7 from both sides
$m = \dfrac{1}{2}$ Divide both sides by 6

When you solve an equation which includes brackets, the first step is to expand the brackets.

EXAMPLE

Solve $8(x + 4) = 3(1 - x) + 7$

$8(x + 4) = 3(1 - x) + 7$
$8x + 32 = 3 - 3x + 7$ Multiply out the brackets
$8x + 32 = 10 - 3x$ Collect like terms
$11x + 32 = 10$ Add $3x$ to both sides
$11x = -22$ Subtract 32 from both sides
$x = -2$ Divide both sides by 11

EXAMINER'S TIP

Equations in the exam will often have solutions that are negative or fractions.

You can check your answer by substituting your solution into each side of the equation and seeing if you get the same number. Try it with this example and you should get 16 on each side.

EXAMPLE

Form and solve an equation to find g.

$2g + 10$
$3g + 20$ g

Because angles in a triangle add to $180°$

$g + 2g + 10 + 3g + 20 = 180$
$6g + 30 = 180$
$6g = 150$
$g = 25$

EXAMINER'S TIP

When questions say 'Form and solve', the final answer by itself will not score full marks.

Exercise AA6

MEDIUM

1 Solve

   a $5x + 2 = 2x + 17$ **b** $8x - 9 = 2x + 15$ **c** $5x + 4 = 3x + 11$

   d $20 - 3x = 2x + 5$ **e** $9x + 15 = 5x - 1$ **f** $8x + 9 = 5x$

   g $\dfrac{7y + 6}{4} = 12$ **h** $1 = \dfrac{3m + 8}{2}$ **i** $\dfrac{6 - x}{5} = 5$

2 The angles of a quadrilateral are $5x$, $10x$, $4x + 12$ and $8x + 24$.

   a Form and solve an equation in x and write down the sizes of all four angles.

   b What sort of quadrilateral is this?

3 Solve

   a $2(x + 3) = 12$ **b** $x = 3(x - 4)$ **c** $3(y - 2) = 2(y + 11)$

   d $6(z + 1) = 2(1 - z)$ **e** $4(x + 1) + 3(2x + 5) = -11$ **f** $3(1 - 2k) - 5(1 - k) = 11$

4 Sam, Kabir and Patrick collect game cards.

   Sam has x cards, Kabir has 10 cards more than Sam, and Patrick
has twice as many cards as Kabir.

   Altogether they have 182 cards.

   a Write an expression in terms of x for the number of cards that

      i Kabir has

      ii Patrick has.

   b Form and solve an equation in x to find out how many cards Sam has.

5 **a** Form and solve an equation to find x.

   b Find the size of each angle of the triangle.

   c What type of triangle is this?

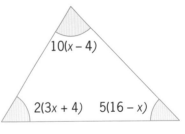

6 Catherine is solving an equation but has made an error.

> $4(x + 1) = 6 - 2(3x + 5)$
> $4x - 4 = 6 - 6x + 10$
> $4x - 4 = 16 - 6x$
> $10x = 20$
> $x = 2$

   a Show by substitution that her solution is wrong.

   b Describe her error.

   c Solve the equation correctly.

UNIT A

The metric and imperial system

Metric system

Length	Mass	Volume and capacity
1 cm = 10 mm	1 g = 1000 mg	1 litre = 1000 ml
1 m = 100 cm	1 kg = 1000 g	1 ml = 1 cm³ (cubic centimetre)
1 m = 1000 mm	1 tonne = 1000 kg	
1 km = 1000 m		

Imperial system

Length	Mass	Volume and capacity
1 foot (ft) = 12 inches	1 pound (lb) = 16 ounces (oz)	1 gallon = 8 pints (pt)
1 yard = 3 feet	1 stone = 14 pounds	

Conversion from metric to imperial units

Length	Mass	Volume and capacity
1 foot ≈ 30 cm	1 kg ≈ 2.2 lb	2 pints ≈ 1 litre
1 mile ≈ 1.6 km	1 lb ≈ 0.5 kg	1 gallon ≈ 4.5 litres
5 miles ≈ 8 km		
3 feet ≈ 1 metre		

Examples

1 Convert 14 m to cm
  1 m = 100 cm
  14 × 100 = 1400 cm

1 Convert 3260 g to kg
  1 kg = 1000 g
  3260 ÷ 1000 = 3.26 kg

1 Convert 3200 cm³ to litres
  3200 ÷ 1000 = 3.2 litres

2 Convert 455 mm to m
  1 m = 1000 mm
  455 ÷ 1000 = 0.455 m

2 Convert 4.63 tonnes to kg
  1 tonne = 1000 kg
  4.63 × 1000 = 4630 kg

2 Convert 9.8 litres to ml
  1 litre = 1000 ml
  9.8 × 1000 = 9800 ml

3 Convert 14 feet into yards
  1 yard = 3 feet
  14 ÷ 3 = 4 yards 2 feet

3 Convert 90 000 000 g to t
  1000 g = 1 kg
  1000 kg = 1 tonne
  90 000 000 ÷ 1000
  = 90 000 kg
  90 000 ÷ 1000 = 90 t

3 Convert 19 pints to gallons
  1 gallon = 8 pints
  19 ÷ 8 = 2.375 gallons
  or 2 gallons and 3 pints

4 Convert 15 miles into km
  5 miles ≈ 8 km
  15 miles ≈ 3 × 8 = 24 km

4 Convert 6 lb to kg
  1 lb ≈ 0.5 kg
  6 × 0.5 = 3 kg

4 Convert 5 litres to pints
  1 litre ≈ 2 pints
  5 litres ≈ 5 × 2 = 10 pints

Exercise AG1

LOW

1 Convert these units as specified.

   a 3 kg to g   **b** 35 mm to cm

   c 4 m to cm   **d** 600 ml to litres

   e 6 gallons to pints   **f** 3.5 feet to inches

   g $2\frac{3}{4}$ stones to pounds   **h** 18 inches to feet

   i 19 lb to stones and pounds   **j** 102 inches to feet and inches

2 Find approximate metric equivalents for these.

   a 4 feet   **b** 15 lb   **c** 4 gallons   **d** 12 pints

3 Find approximate imperial equivalents for these.

   a 200 cm   **b** 25 km   **c** 12 kg   **d** 14 litres

4 It is about 158 miles from Swansea to Southampton. How far is this approximately in km?

5 Convert 5 feet 10 inches into

   a cm   **b** m

6 Given that there are 16 oz in one pound add together 4 lb 3 oz and 9 lb 15 oz.

7 'Chuckon' paint can be purchased in either 2 litre or 5 litre tins. Approximately how many more pints does the larger tin hold?

8 Gavin's family own a caravan which is 16 feet long and 8 feet wide. Will it fit into their driveway which is 5 metres long and 2.5 metres wide?

9 A small hotel swimming pool contains 24 000 gallons of water.

   a How many litres does the pool contain?

   b Ralph decides to empty the pool using his 15-litre bucket. If it takes Ralph 30 seconds to fill and empty his bucket how long will it take him to empty the pool? Give your answer in appropriate units.

10 ☆ EXAM-STYLE QUESTION ☆

> Jacob weighs $9\frac{1}{2}$ stone. A £1 coin weighs approximately 9.5 g. If Jacob is given his weight in pound coins what will he be worth?

Using a ruler and protractor you need to be able to construct a triangle given one side and two angles.

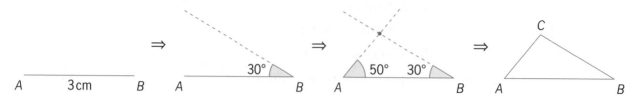

Using only a ruler and a pair of compasses you need to be able to construct:

- A triangle with three given sides

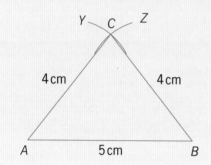

Construct a triangle with sides 5 cm, 4 cm, 4 cm.

Draw a line AB = 5 cm long

With the compasses set to 4 cm and the point on A, draw an arc Y.

With the same compass setting, and the point on B, draw an arc Z.

Label the point of intersection of the arcs C.

Join A and B to C to form the triangle.

- The bisector of an angle

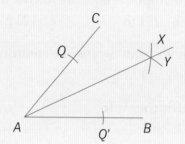

With the compass point on A draw arcs on AC and AB at Q and Q'.

With the compass point at Q, and then Q', with the same compass setting, draw arcs X and Y.

Join A to the intersection of X and Y.

- The perpendicular bisector of a line segment AB

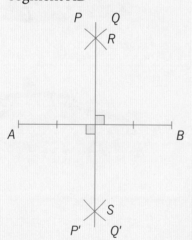

With the compass point on A draw arcs P and P'.

Using the same setting and the compass point on B draw arcs Q and Q' to intersect at R and S.

Join RS.

- The perpendicular at a point on a line

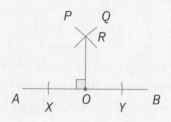

With the compass point on O draw arcs X and Y on AB.

Extend the compasses and with the point on X, then Y, draw arcs P and Q to intersect at R.

Join OR.

- The perpendicular from a point T to a line AB

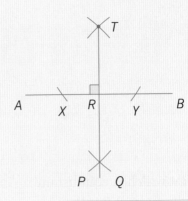

With the compass point on *T* draw arcs *X* and *Y* on *AB*.
With the same compass setting and the compass point on *X*, then *Y*, draw arcs *P* and *Q* on the opposite side of the line from *T*.
Draw a line joining *T* to the intersection of arcs *P* and *Q* and mark the point *R* where this line crosses the line *AB*.
TR is the perpendicular from *T* to *AB*.

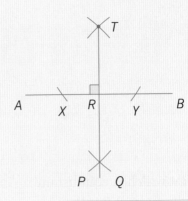 labels: *T*, *A*, *X*, *R*, *Y*, *B*, *P*, *Q*

Exercise AG2

MEDIUM

1 Copy the diagrams (you can make them larger) and construct

  a the perpendicular bisector of line *AB*

  b the bisector of angle *AOB*.

2 Copy the diagrams and construct

  a the perpendicular bisector of *AB*

  b the perpendicular from *P* to *AB*.

3 Construct a triangle with sides 3 cm, 4 cm and 5 cm. Measure all three angles of the triangle. What special sort of triangle is it?

4 Construct an equilateral triangle with sides 7 cm. Construct a perpendicular from the apex (top) of your triangle to the base and measure the length of this perpendicular.

5 Construct a triangle *ABC* with *CB* = 7.4 cm, angle *C* = 60° and angle *B* = 48°. Measure the size of the third angle.

6 Construct an equilateral triangle *PQR* with sides 9 cm. From each vertex of the triangle construct a perpendicular to the opposite side.
These lines are called **altitudes** of the triangle. If your construction is accurate these three altitudes will intersect at a common point.

7 **a** Construct a triangle with sides 10 cm, 8 cm and 7 cm.
  b Construct the angle bisectors of all three angles.
  c Label the point *O* where these bisectors intersect and construct a perpendicular to one of the three sides of your triangle from *O*. Label the foot of this perpendicular *T*.
  Using *O* as your centre and *OT* as your radius draw the in-circle of the triangle (the circle which has the three sides of the triangle as tangents).

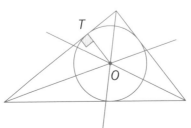

The locus of a point is the set of all positions it can occupy given certain constraining conditions.

- A locus can be a line, a curve or a region.

Here are some common examples.

The locus of a point which is a constant distance 3 cm from a fixed point O is a circle of radius 3 cm. 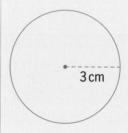	The locus of a point which is equidistant from two fixed points A and B is the perpendicular bisector of the line segment joining A to B. 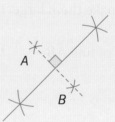
The locus of a point which is a constant distance from a fixed line is a pair of parallel lines. 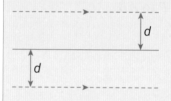	The locus of a point which is equidistant from two lines OA and OB is the bisector of angle AOB. 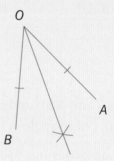

EXAMPLE

Show the locus of points which are 2 cm from the line segment AB.

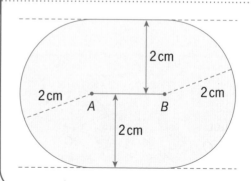

To draw the locus from points A and B, place a pair of compasses, set to 2 cm, on the points and draw two semicircles to join up with the line as shown.

Exercise AG3

1 Copy the diagram, making it larger, and construct these loci.
   a The locus of point *P* which is always 2 cm from *B*.
   b The locus of point *R* which is equidistant from the line segments *AB* and *AC* and is inside the triangle *ABC*.
   c The locus of point *Q* which is equidistant from points *A* and *C*.

2 *WX*, *XY*, *YZ* and *ZW* are hedges surrounding a field. *P* is a pole in the ground.
   Copy the diagram and construct and describe the following loci.
   a The locus of a football that is kicked so that it is always the same distance from *X* as from *Z*.
   b The locus of a sheep which moves from the hedge *ZY* to the corner *W* so that it remains equidistant from *WX* and *WZ*.
   c A goat is chained to a stake at *P*. When taut the rope extends to *W*. Shade the region the goat can reach.

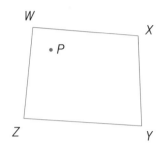

3 Two villages, *A* and *B*, are 20 km apart. *B* is due south of *A*. The fire brigade from village *A* looks after a region 10 km around *A*, while the fire brigade from village *B* looks after a region 12 km around *B*.
   Using a scale of 1 cm for 4 km draw a diagram to show the region covered by both fire brigades.

4 A guard dog is on a leash 6 m long. The leash is attached to the corner of a building as shown.

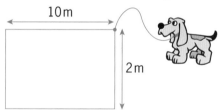

   a Make an accurate scale drawing and sketch the region which the dog can guard.
   b Draw two more diagrams to show the regions the dog can guard if the leash is
      i 9 m long   ii 11 m long.

Maps and bearings

The diagram shows the key points of the compass.

The key word in a bearing statement is **from**. The bearing of B **from** A tells you that the north line is drawn at A while the bearing of A **from** B tells you that the north line is to be drawn at B. Here are some examples of bearings. You should check them by measuring the bearings yourself.

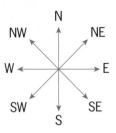

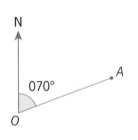 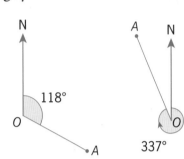

To find an angle like this, accurately measure the small angle and subtract from 360°.

Bearings have 3 digit, for example 080°.

EXAMPLE

On what bearing are you travelling when you go

a north **b** south **c** south-west **d** north-east?

....

a 000° **b** 180° **c** 225° **d** 045°

EXAMPLE

If Suzi travels on a bearing of 315° for 8 km starting at her house, show on a scale drawing her position relative to her house. Use a scale of 1 cm for 2 km.
If you do a rough sketch first this will help you get an idea of how much space you need for your drawing.

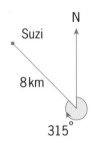

A scale is essential to make sense of a map. Map scales are given in the form $1 : n$, which means, for example, that 1 cm on the map represents n centimetres in the real world.

EXAMPLE

Interpret the meaning of these scales.

a $1 : 200\,000$
  1 cm = 200 000 cm
     = 200 000 ÷ 100 m
     = 2000 m
     = 2000 ÷ 1000 km
     = 2 km

b $1 : 1\,000\,000$
  1 cm = 1 000 000 cm
     = 1 000 000 ÷ 100 m
     = 10 000 m
     = 10 000 ÷ 1000 km
     = 10 km

c $1 : 40$
  1 cm = 40 cm
     = 40 ÷ 100 m
     = 0.4 m

Using a scale of 1 cm for 1 km make a scale drawing of the following journey.

Susanne walks 7 km from X to Y on a bearing of 130°. She then walks 6 km from Y to Z on a bearing of 210°. She then walks directly from Z back to X. How far has she walked in total and on what bearing does she travel to get from Z to X?

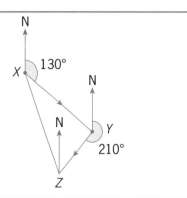

Distance on scale drawing from Z to X is 5 cm, therefore real distance = 5 km.

The bearing is 360° − 15° = 345°

Exercise AG4

MEDIUM

1 Using a protractor measure the bearing of B from A in these diagrams.

a

b

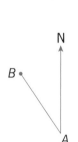

c

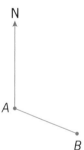

2 Which compass directions correspond to the following bearings?
   a 270°   **b** 045°   **c** 315°

3 A ship sails on a bearing of 200° until it reaches its destination. If it returns on the same route, what is the bearing of the return journey?

4 **a** Describe the journey which begins at A and finishes at C in terms of the distance travelled and bearings.
   b By scale drawing, find the direct distance of C from A.

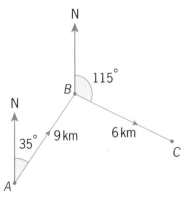

5 The scale of a map is 1 : 5 000 000.
   a How many km does 1 cm represent?
   b How many cm represent 14.5 km?
   c How many km are represented by 8.5 cm?

6 Why would a scale 1 : 6 000 000 not be appropriate if Max wants to do a scale drawing of his house?
   Suggest a more appropriate scale, explaining your answer carefully.

Pythagoras' theorem describes the relationship between the lengths of the sides of a **right-angled** triangle.

$a^2 + b^2 = c^2$ or $c^2 = a^2 + b^2$

(short side)^2 + (short side)^2 = (hypotenuse)^2

Pythagoras allows you to find one side of a right-angled triangle if you know the other two sides.

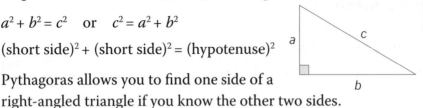

> The longest side of a right-angled triangle is called the **hypotenuse**.

EXAMPLE

Find the length x in these triangles. Give your answers to 3 sf.

a

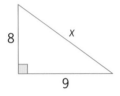

8   x

9

b

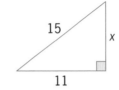

15   x

11

> When you have to find one of the shorter sides you have to do a subtraction.

The missing side is the hypotenuse.

$$x^2 = 9^2 + 8^2$$
$$= 81 + 64 = 145$$
$$x = \sqrt{145} = 12.0\,\text{cm (3 sf)}$$

This time a shorter side is missing.

$$x^2 = 15^2 - 11^2$$
$$= 225 - 121 = 104$$
$$x = \sqrt{104} = 10.2\,\text{cm (3 sf)}$$

> Do not round until the final answer. Write units in your answer.

EXAMPLE

Find the distance between the points with coordinates $A(1, 1)$ and $B(4, 6)$.

Construct a right-angled triangle with A and B as the end-points of its hypotenuse.

$$AB^2 = 5^2 + 3^2 = 34$$
$$AB = \sqrt{34} = 5.83 \text{ units}$$

> Write 'units' since you are not told what the units of measurement are.

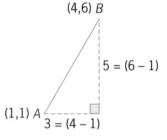

(4,6) B

5 = (6 − 1)

(1,1) A

3 = (4 − 1)

EXAMPLE

Calculate the length of the longest ruler that could be placed inside a box with dimensions $10\,\text{cm} \times 6\,\text{cm} \times 4\,\text{cm}$.

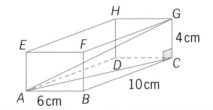

H   G

E   F   4 cm

D   C

10 cm

A   6 cm   B

First consider the base $ABCD$ and calculate the length of the diagonal AC.

$$AC^2 = 10^2 + 6^2$$
$$AC = \sqrt{136}$$

> Leave your answer in this form or keep the full calculator answer saved to avoid rounding errors.

Next consider the triangle ACG and calculate the hypotenuse AG.

$$AG^2 = (\sqrt{136})^2 + 4^2 = 136 + 16 = 152$$
Hence $AG = \sqrt{152} = 12.3\,\text{m}$

> You can now round your final answer.

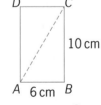

D   C

10 cm

A   6 cm   B

G

4 cm

A $\sqrt{136}$ cm   C

Exercise AG5

In this exercise, give your answes to 3 significant figures where appropriate.

1 Find the missing sides in these triangles.

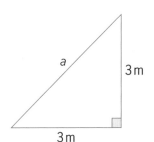
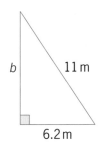
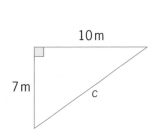
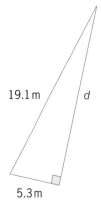

2 Find the length of the diagonal of a square of side 10 m.

3 Find the length of the longest straight line that can be drawn on a piece of A5 paper with dimensions 5.8 inches × 8.3 inches.

4 Mark walks 400 m east and then 250 m south.
   How far is Mark from his starting point?

5 a Find the distance between the points with coordinates (0, 5) and (−7, 0).

   ← Draw a sketch.

   b Find a general formula for the distance between two points (p, q) and (r, t).

6 Do you think 7 cm, 17 cm and 15 cm could be the lengths of a right-angled triangle? Explain your answer carefully.

7 The diagonal of a square is 12 m long. Find its area.   ← Label the side of the square x.

8 Find the lengths x and y in this diagram.

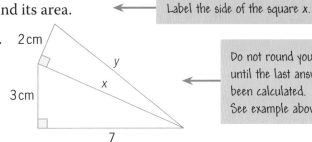

Do not round your answer until the last answer has been calculated.
See example above.

9 Find the length a in this diagram.

10 What is the length of the longest pole that can be placed inside a cube with side of length 15 m?

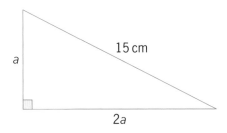

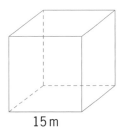

UNIT A

Core trigonometry

Trigonometry enables you to solve problems associated with right-angled triangles.

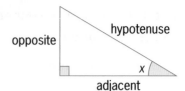

$$\text{Sine } x = \frac{\text{Opposite}}{\text{Hypotenuse}} \quad \text{Cosine } x = \frac{\text{Adjacent}}{\text{Hypotenuse}} \quad \text{Tangent } x = \frac{\text{Opposite}}{\text{Adjacent}}$$

One way to remember the definitions is by the mnemonic: SOHCAHTOA

$$\text{Sin } x = \frac{O}{H}$$

$$\text{Cos } x = \frac{A}{H}$$

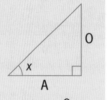

$$\text{Tan } x = \frac{O}{A}$$

You can find the values of the sine, cosine and tangent of an angle on your calculator.
Make sure the calculator is set to degree mode.

EXAMPLE

Find the sides and angles marked with letters in these diagrams.

a

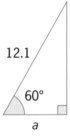

12.1

60°

a

b

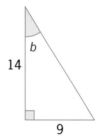

14

b

9

c

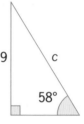

9

c

58°

---

a $\cos 60° = \dfrac{a}{12.1}$

$a = 12.1 \cos 60°$

$= 6.05 \text{ cm}$

b $\tan b = \dfrac{9}{14}$

$b = \tan^{-1}(9 \div 14) = 32.7°$

(to find a missing angle you need to use shift-tan)

c $\sin 58° = \dfrac{9}{c}$

$c \sin 58° = 9$

$c = 9 \div \sin 58° = 10.6 \text{ (3 sf)}$

EXAMPLE

A plane taking off from Gatwick gains an altitude of 2.3 km after travelling 9 km. At what angle is the plane climbing?

Use sine to solve the problem.

$\sin\theta = \dfrac{2.3}{9}$ $\qquad \theta = \sin^{-1}[(2.3 \div 9)] = 14.8°$

9 km

2.3 km

G

θ

EXAMPLE

A ship travels due east from X to B, a distance of 78 km. It then travels due south to C which is 47 km from B. What is the bearing of C from X?

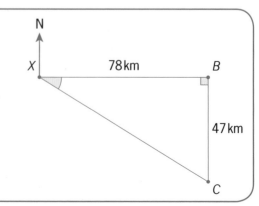

$\tan C = \dfrac{47}{78}$ $\qquad C = \tan^{-1} \dfrac{47}{78} = 31.1°$

The bearing of C from $X = 90° + 31.1° = 121.1° = 121°$ (3 sf)

Exercise AG6

1 Find the lengths and angles marked with letters in these diagrams (all lengths are in cm).

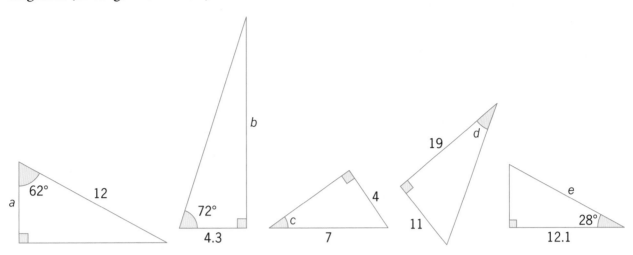

2 Find the angle labelled x in this isosceles triangle.

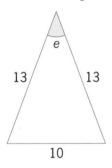

3 A drainage pipe is laid along the diagonal of a rectangular field of width 40 m and length 65 m.
What is the angle between the shorter side of the field and the pipe?

4 From the top of a 30 m cliff the angle of depression to a small boat is 28°.
How far from the foot of the cliff is the boat?

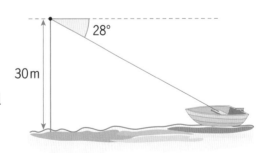

5 A yacht sails from Dingle on a bearing of 255°. By the end of the day it has travelled 42 km.
How far west of Dingle is the yacht at the end of the day?

6 Seema stood 5 m from the foot of a tree. She measured the angle of elevation of the top of the tree as 57° and the angle of depression of the base of the tree as 22°.

   a Find the height *TH*.
   b Find the height of the tree.
   c How tall is Seema approximately?

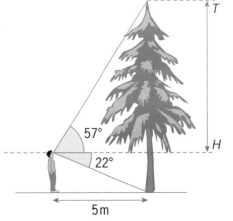

Collecting data

AS1

- **Primary** data is data that you collect yourself.
  You can collect data from a **survey** or an **experiment**.

- **Secondary** data is data taken from an existing source such
  as newspapers or the internet.

- Data can be **discrete** or **continuous**.

You can count discrete data, for example the number of eggs in a nest. Continuous data is data you measure, for example weight on height.

- A **two-way table** shows two sets of data about the same
  group of people or things, for example, hair colour and
  eye colour.

		Hair colour			
		Blonde	Brown	Red	Black
Eye colour	Blue				
	Grey				
	Green				
	Brown				

When collecting data, you need to choose a **sample** that is
not biased.

Choose a **random sample**, assign a number to each possible
member of the group and use a random number generator to
pick numbers.

Bias can happen when you only ask your friends or only ask people in a certain age group. In general the larger the sample size the more reliable the data analysis.

To find a 20% **systematic sample** start from a random
value, say the 3rd value and then choose every 5th

$(20\% = \frac{1}{5})$ value, that is 3rd, 8th, 13th, 18th, 23rd, ...

In all types of sampling first assign a number to each possible data value.

In a **stratified sample** divide the population into groups
and choose a random sample from each group in the
ratio of their sizes.

- **Questionnaires** should be relevant and useful to your
  survey.

Use clear language. Cover all options and leave no gaps between the answer choices.

EXAMPLE

This question appeared in a survey about time spent using a mobile phone.

> How much time do you spend on your mobile phone?
> Less then 5 minutes ☐   Up to 10 minutes ☐   Over an hour ☐

Criticise the question, and write a better question.

....

The question does not have a time frame.
It does not specify how the time is spent: just making phone calls,
or also listening to music, playing games and so on.
The answer choices have gaps and overlaps.
How long, on average, do you spend making calls on your mobile each day?

Less than 10 minutes   ☐   10–30 minutes   ☐   Over 30 minutes   ☐

38   Collecting data

A machine produces buttons.
Three workers use the machine
and produce these numbers of buttons.

Abi – 5890   Ben – 4140   Carly – 6770

Their supervisor wants to take a stratified
sample of 400 of these buttons for
quality control purposes.
Work out how many she should sample
from Abi, Ben and Carly.

Total produced 5890 + 4140 + 6770 = 16 800

Abi $400 \times \dfrac{5890}{16\,800} = 140.2$ so 140 buttons

Ben $400 \times \dfrac{4140}{16\,800} = 98.6$ so 99 buttons

Carly $400 \times \dfrac{6770}{16\,800} = 161.2$ so 161 buttons

Check 140 + 99 + 161 = 400

Work out the total. Find the fraction of 400
for each person. Check that the total of your
three samples is 400.

Exercise AS1

 MEDIUM HIGH

1   Design an observation sheet to collect data on colour and type of
    vehicle in a road traffic survey.

2   a   Design an observation sheet to collect data on women's shoe sizes
        and glove sizes. You may assume shoe sizes range from 3 to 8
        and glove sizes range from extra small to large.
    b   A survey gave the following information.
            7 women had shoe size 5 and glove size medium
            9 women had shoe size 4 and glove size small
        Add this information to your observation sheet.

3   Anja was carrying out a survey on how much people spent on food each week.
    On a Tuesday morning she asked 100 people at the supermarket
    closest to where she lives.
    a   Explain why Anja's survey might be biased.
    b   Describe a better method for Anja to choose her sample.

4   Below are the questions to be used in a survey on hair products.
    Some of the questions are not suitable.
    Write down what is wrong with them and write better questions.
    a   What colour is your hair?   Blonde   Brown   Black
    b   Is your hair dyed?   Yes   No
    c   How long is your hair?   Short   Medium   Long
    d   How many times per week do you wash your hair?
                                          Once   Twice   Every day
    e   Do you always use conditioner?   Yes   No   Sometimes

5   A school has 880 students. An alphabetical list of all the students is produced.
    Explain why taking every eighth student from the list may not produce
    a suitable sample of the school's students.

Averages

- An **average** is a representative value of a set of data.
- The **mode** is the data value that occurs most often.
- In grouped data the **modal class** is the class with the highest frequency density.
- The **median** is the middle number when data are arranged in order.
- In grouped data you can find the class in which the median lies but not an actual median value.
- The **mean** is calculated by adding all the data values then dividing by the number of pieces of data.
- In grouped data you calculate an **estimated mean** using the midpoint and the frequency of each class.

> If there are two middle numbers the median is the middle value of these two, for example, in the data set
> 2   2   4   5   7   8   10   11   the middle values are 5 and 7 so the median is 6.

> To find the median in a small data set find the $\frac{1}{2}(n + 1)$th value where n = number of items in the data.
> Imagine listing the numbers of pins in order – 50 would be the 18th number in the list.

EXAMPLE

On boxes of drawing pins the average contents are labelled as 50.
The table shows the numbers of drawing pins in 35 boxes.

Drawing pins	48	49	50	51	52	53	54
Frequency	3	6	21	1	2	1	1

Joni says that the average is 50, whatever measure of average is used.
Explain why Joni is correct.

The mode is 50, as 50 has the highest frequency (21).

For 35 boxes, the middle value is
$\frac{1}{2}(35 + 1)$ = 18th value, 3 + 6 = 9, 9 + 21 = 30
So the 18th value, the median = 50
Total number of pins = 48 × 3 + 49 × 6 + 50 × 21
$$+ 51 + 52 × 2 + 53 + 54$$
$$= 1750$$
mean = 1750 ÷ 35 = 50
All three types of average give an answer of 50, so Joni is correct.

EXAMPLE

The table summarises the number of miles Reuben cycled each day for the first 29 days in April.

Miles cycled, m	$0 \leq m < 20$	$20 \leq m < 40$	$40 \leq m < 60$	$60 \leq m < 80$
Frequency	5	9	11	4

a   Work out an estimate of the mean number of miles Reuben cycled.

b   How many miles could Reuben cycle on April 30th so that the class interval in which the median lies does not change? Explain your answer.

a   Total number of miles = 10 × 5 + 30 × 9 + 50 × 11 + 70 × 4 = 1150 (using midpoints of classes)
    1150 ÷ 29 = 39.655... so the mean = 39.7 miles

b $\frac{1}{2}(29 + 1)$ = 15th value 5 + 9 = 14, so 15th value, the median, is in the class $40 \leq m < 60$.
    With 30 values median will be $\frac{1}{2}(30 + 1)$ = 15.5th value,
    so you average the 15th and 16th values. Both of these must be in the class $40 \leq m < 60$ for the median to stay where it is.
    So on April 30th Reuben must cycle a distance of 40 miles or more.

> Estimate does not mean guess. Use the frequency and the midpoint of each class. Remember to divide by the total frequency, not the number of classes.

Exercise AS2

MEDIUM

1 Henry drew this table to show the number of tracks
on each of the CDs he owned.

Number of tracks	7	8	9	10	11
Number of CDs	4	6	12	5	2

   a   Write down   i the median   ii the mode number of tracks.

   b   Work out the mean number of tracks.

2 The numbers and prices of theatre tickets available for a
performance are shown in the table.

Ticket price (£)	50	40	25	15
Number available	140	50	200	10

   a   Calculate the mean price of a ticket.

   b   For a special performance one evening all ticket prices were reduced by £5.
      What was the mean price of a ticket for that performance?

3 The numbers of hats of different hat sizes sold by a department store are given in the table.

Hat size	$6\frac{3}{8}$	$6\frac{1}{2}$	$6\frac{5}{8}$	$6\frac{3}{4}$	$6\frac{7}{8}$	7	$7\frac{1}{8}$	$7\frac{1}{4}$	$7\frac{3}{8}$	$7\frac{1}{2}$	$7\frac{5}{8}$
Number sold	1	0	2	3	8	15	12	3	0	0	0

When the manager of the store orders new hats to sell which type of average
should he use? Give reasons for your answer and show your calculations.

4 The table shows the times a sample of 84 students spent doing
homework one evening.

Time, m (min)	$0 < m \le 20$	$20 < m \le 40$	$40 < m \le 60$	$60 < m \le 80$	$80 < m \le 100$	$100 < m \le 120$
Frequency	1	21	11	22	8	21

   a   Work out an estimate of the mean time.

   b   Which class contains the median?

   c   Explain why the modal class may not be a good measure of average
      to use with these data.

5 Ahmed recorded the number of hours of sunshine in May and June.

May

Number of hours sunshine, h	Number of days
$0 \le h < 2$	5
$2 \le h < 4$	14
$4 \le h < 6$	7
$6 \le h < 8$	5

June

Number of hours sunshine, h	Number of days
$0 \le h < 2$	5
$2 \le h < 4$	7
$4 \le h < 6$	10
$6 \le h < 8$	8

   a   Calculate estimates of the mean number of hours of sunshine in May and in June.

   b   Write down, for both May and June

      i   the class which contains the median   ii the modal class.

Comparing data

- When you use graphs to compare data sets always make comparisons between the same type of average (means, medians or modes), the range or the IQR.
- The **range** = largest value – smallest value
- The **interquartile range (IQR)** = **upper quartile** – **lower quartile** (UQ – LQ)
  - ➤ To find the quartiles put the data in order, then

    $\frac{1}{4}$ of the values ≤ LQ $\frac{3}{4}$ of the values ≤ UQ

    For small data sets find $\frac{1}{4}$ and $\frac{3}{4}$ of $(n + 1)$th value where n is the number of items in the data.
- You can use a **stem-and-leaf diagram** to display small data sets.
  - ➤ The stem is written on one side of a vertical line with leaves on the other side.
  - ➤ Leaves are written in order with the smallest next to the stem.
  - ➤ Always write a key.

EXAMPLE

The times taken, in seconds, for 19 children to complete a jigsaw are

    69   103   94   65   88   76   78   93   105   112

    83   98   85   89   91   76   87   90   82

a Draw a stem-and-leaf diagram to display these data.

b 19 adults completed the same jigsaw. Their results are summarised as median 76 seconds, IQR 20 seconds. Compare the times of the children and the adults.

a

```
11 | 2
10 | 3  5
 9 | 0  1  3  4  8
 8 | 2  3  5  7  8  9
 7 | 6  6  8
 6 | 5  9        Key: 8 | 2 means 82 seconds
```

b Median for children $\frac{1}{2}(19 + 1)$th = 10th value = 88 seconds, so on average the adults were faster.

IQR for children 94 – 78 = 16 seconds which is lower than the adults' so the children's results were more consistent.

⊠ You can use a **frequency polygon** to display continuous data that has been grouped into classes.

> Plot each frequency with the midpoint of the class. Join the points with straight lines using a ruler.

EXAMPLE

Compare the profits (or losses) for these samples of retailers and manufacturers.

On average the retailers made more profit as their modal class (£20 000–£40 000) is higher than the modal class (£0–£20 000) for the manufacturers.

> Always compare classes, not individual values or peaks.

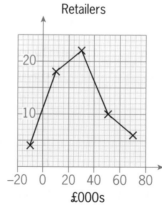

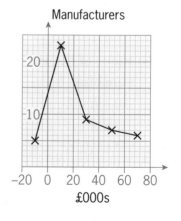

Exercise AS3

1 These are the times taken, to the nearest minute, to deliver leaflets to 15 roads.

  22 15 28 34 29 9 11 24 23 16 20 30 31 32 41

Represent these data on a stem-and-leaf diagram.

2 The average attendance, to the nearest 100, at some football games in 2009/10 were as follows.

  4600 4300 4100 2800 3900 3700 6000 3600 2400 4000
  1800 2500 2700 3400 2400 1800 2100 2500 7500 2200

Represent these data on a stem-and-leaf diagram.

3 The back-to-back stem-and-leaf diagram shows the lengths of samples of two different species of caterpillar.

```
    Species A          Species B
          5  4 | 7 | 2
       9  4  3 | 6 | 0  1  5
       7  7  5 | 5 | 2  3  4  6  7  8
    9  8  5  3 | 4 | 0  1  9  9
  7  5  4  3 | 3 | 1  4  5  6
       6  4  1 | 2 | 9
```

Key: 1 | 2 | 9 means 21 mm for species A and 29 mm for species B.
Make three comparisons between these samples of species of caterpillars.

Leaf length, l (mm)	Frequency
$20 < l \le 30$	2
$30 < l \le 40$	3
$40 < l \le 50$	11
$50 < l \le 60$	0
$60 < l \le 70$	0
$70 < l \le 80$	6
$80 < l \le 90$	5
$90 < l \le 100$	3

4 Todd measured the lengths, in mm, of leaves dropped from trees in his garden one day in autumn. The data he collected are summarised in the table.

  a Draw a frequency polygon to show the length of the leaves.

  b Explain how the data suggest that there may be more than one type of tree in Todd's garden.

5 In a triathlon there are transition times when competitors change sport from swim to bike and then from bike to run. Paolo collected data on the transition times, in seconds, for 80 competitors. These are the transition times for swim to bike.

Time, s (seconds)	$120 < s \le 150$	$150 < s \le 180$	$180 < s \le 210$	$210 < s \le 240$	$240 < s \le 270$
Frequency	12	21	26	15	6

  a Draw a frequency polygon to represent these data.

  Paolo drew this frequency polygon for the transition times for bike to run.

  b Compare the transition times taken for swim to bike and for bike to run.

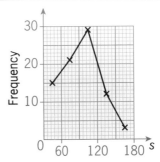

- You can use a **box plot** to show how data are spread.

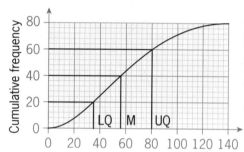

lowest value | lower quartile (LQ) | median | upper quartile (UQ) | highest value

➤ If the **median** is closer to the **LQ** than the **UQ** the data is positively skewed.
➤ If the median is closer to the UQ than the LQ the data is negatively skewed.
➤ For data sets LQ is the $\frac{1}{4}(n+1)$th value and UQ is the $\frac{3}{4}(n+1)$th value.

- You use a **cumulative frequency graph** to represent large amounts of grouped data.
- You can estimate the median, the LQ, the UQ and the **IQR** from a cumulative frequency graph.
- You can use the median and IQR to draw a box plot.

To find the lower quartile draw a horizontal line from $\frac{1}{4}$ of the maximum cumulative frequency (CF) on the vertical axis across to the graph. From this point draw a vertical line down to the horizontal axis and read off the LQ = 35. Use $\frac{1}{2}$ of the maximum CF to find the median = 56 and $\frac{3}{4}$ of the maximum CF for the UQ = 80.

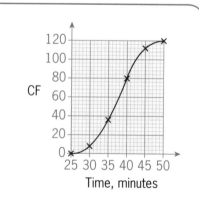

EXAMPLE

The box plots summarise the times taken by boys and girls to complete a sudoku. Give one similarity and one difference between the times taken by the girls and the times taken by the boys.

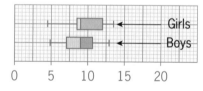

Similarity: They have the same median; they have the same IQR.
Difference: Range for boys is smaller than range for girls; girls' times are negatively skewed, while boys' times are not skewed.

Don't be tempted to compare individual values such as only the lowest values, or different values such as girls' median greater than boys' LQ when making comparisons.

EXAMPLE

The cumulative frequency diagram summarises the times taken by 120 people to swim a mile.
a What was the median time?
b This quote came from a news report.
'The range of times taken to swim a mile was 23 minutes, the quickest time was 28 minutes'
Could this quote be accurate? Explain your answer.

a 38 minutes   b Range 23 is possible: 23 < 50 − 25

Quickest time 28 is possible: interval 25 to 30 has 7 people.
But 28 + 23 = 51 and 51 cannot be longest time, so the quote is not accurate.

Exercise AS4

1 One year a school held a summer fete and a winter craft fair.
The age distribution for each is summarised in these box plots.
Compare the age distributions at these events.

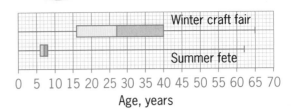

0 5 10 15 20 25 30 35 40 45 50 55 60 65 70
Age, years

2 In a triathlon there are transition times when competitors change sport from swim to bike and then from bike to run. Paolo collected data on the transition times, in seconds, for 80 competitors.
These are the transition times for swim to bike.

Time, s (seconds)	$120 < s \leq 150$	$150 < s \leq 180$	$180 < s \leq 210$	$210 < s \leq 240$	$240 < s \leq 270$
Frequency	12	21	26	15	6

a Draw a cumulative frequency graph to represent this information.

Paolo drew this box plot for the transition times for bike to run.

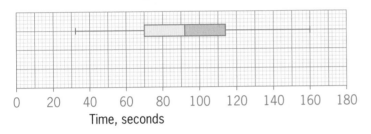

0   20   40   60   80   100   120   140   160   180
Time, seconds

b Find suitable measures from both graphs to compare the transition times taken for swim to bike and for bike to run.

3 The table summarises the times, in minutes, that students arrived before the start of an exam at a school.

Time, t (minutes)	$0 \leq t < 4$	$4 \leq t < 8$	$8 \leq t < 12$	$12 \leq t < 16$	$16 \leq t < 20$	$20 \leq t < 24$	$24 \leq t < 28$
No. of students	6	18	24	46	64	30	12

a Draw a cumulative frequency table.
b Draw a cumulative frequency graph.
c Use your graph to find estimates of the number of people who arrived
   i within 10 minutes before the start of the exam
   ii over 22 minutes before the exam began.
d The first student arrived for the exam 27 minutes early, the last student arrived as the exam was about to start. Estimate the other measures needed and draw a box plot for these data.

4 The times taken for 120 people to complete a run are summarised in this report.
'The fastest time to complete the run was 22 minutes, with the first 18 people finishing in under $\frac{1}{2}$ hour. In total 60 people finished within 40 minutes. Only 17 people took over 50 minutes and, of these, five people took longer than an hour, with the final time recorded as 68 minutes.'
a Draw a cumulative frequency graph to represent this information.
b Use the information and the graph to draw a box plot.

Histograms

- You use a **histogram** to represent continuous data – usually the data are grouped in classes.
- Each **bar** of the histogram represents one **class**.
- The **frequency** of a class is represented by the area of the bar.
- The width of the bar is the **class interval**.
- Class intervals can be different widths.
- The height of a bar is the **frequency density** of the class.
- Frequency density is shown on the vertical axis.
- **Frequency density = frequency ÷ class width**
- On a histogram the **modal class** may not be the highest bar.
- If the histogram bars peak in the middle with the bars on either side approximately the same height the data are not skewed.
- If the bars peak towards the lower end of the data (on the left of the histogram) the data have **positive skew**.
- If the bars peak towards the higher end of the data (on the right of the histogram) the data have **negative skew**.

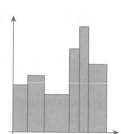

> The highest bar might not be the same as the class with the greatest frequency as the class intervals might not be the same.

EXAMPLE

The table summarises the speeds, v mph, of 80 vehicles travelling along Berry Road.

Speed, v mph	$15 < v \leq 30$	$30 < v \leq 35$	$35 < v \leq 60$	$60 < v \leq 70$
Number of vehicles	24	19	30	7

a   Draw a histogram to represent these data.

b   The speed limit for the road is 40 mph.
    Estimate how many of the cars were exceeding the speed limit.

c   Speeds of 80 vehicles travelling on Cherry Road were found to have a median in the class $15 < v \leq 30$.
    Comment on the different speeds of vehicles in these two roads.

> Frequency density = frequency ÷ class width

a

Class width	$30 - 15 = 15$	$35 - 30 = 5$	$60 - 35 = 25$	$70 - 60 = 10$
Frequency density	$24 \div 15 = 1.6$	$19 \div 5 = 3.8$	$30 \div 25 = 1.2$	$7 \div 10 = 0.7$

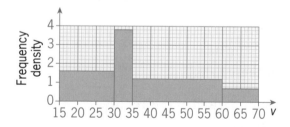

> Be clear which data you are referring to when writing comments.

b   Area of bars above 40 mph = $1.2 \times 20 + 0.7 \times 10 = 24 + 7 = 31$ so 31 cars were speeding.

c   On Berry Road the median is in class $30 < v \leq 35$ ($\frac{1}{2}$ of 80 = 40 and 24 + 19 = 43, so the 40th value must be in class $30 < v \leq 35$), compared with $15 < v \leq 30$ on Cherry Road so over half the cars are travelling faster on Berry Road than Cherry Road.

Exercise AS5

1 Jenny asked a group of men about their weekly consumption of units of alcohol.

She summarised her results in this table.

Units of alcohol, u	0	0 < u ≤ 1	1 < u ≤ 7	7 < u ≤ 15	15 < u ≤ 30	Over 30
Number of people	8	12	27	30	21	9

   a The last group 'Over 30' is open-ended. Choose a suitable value for this last group and use it to draw a histogram to represent these data.

   b The 'low risk' consumption for men is less than 21 units of alcohol per week. Calculate an estimate of the number of men who would be considered low risk.

2 The table summarises survey data about the average hours men worked per week.

Hours worked, h	0 ≤ h < 6	6 ≤ h < 15	15 ≤ h < 30	30 ≤ h < 42	42 ≤ h < 60
Frequency	3	9	27	69	42

   a Draw a histogram to represent these data.

   b Estimate the number of men who work more than 40 hours a week.

The histogram summarises survey data about the average hours women worked per week.

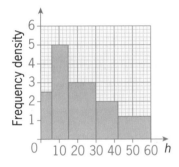

   c Explain how the graph shows that the same number of women worked 6 to 15 hours as 15 to 30 hours.

   d Write down two comparisons between the average hours men and women worked in the survey.

3 The incomplete table and incomplete diagram show the expected journey times to work for a sample of city workers.

Time, t (min)	0 < t ≤ 20	20 < t ≤ 30	30 < t ≤ 40	40 < t ≤ 45	45 < t ≤ 60	60 < t ≤ 90
Number		16		28	33	21

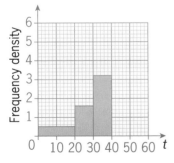

   a Copy and complete the table and the diagram.

   b Estimate the number of city workers in the sample whose journey time is longer than 50 minutes.

Arithmetic with integers and decimals (BN1)

You should be able to add and subtract integers and decimals without using a calculator.

← LOOK BACK

See topic AN1 on page 2 to revise multiplying and dividing with negative numbers.

EXAMPLE

Calculate

a 12.3 + 0.04 + 5.1   **b** 5.6 + 9 + 1.54

c 12 − 4.5   **d** 6.3 − 4.16

a 12.3
    0.04
 +5.1
 17.44

b 5.6
  9.
 +1.54
 16.14

c 12.0
 − 4.5
  7.5

d 6.30
 − 4.16
  2.14

> After every **whole number** there is an invisible decimal point.

EXAMPLE

Colin works out 4.1 + 12 like this:

$$\begin{array}{r} 4.1 \\ +1\,2 \\ \hline 5.3 \end{array}$$

Explain what he has done wrong and work out the correct answer.

Colin forgot the decimal point after the 12 and got the numbers out of line.

$$\begin{array}{r} 4.1 \\ +12. \\ \hline 16.1 \end{array}$$

> It is important to **always** line up the decimal points in a single column.

Sometimes you can use place value facts to multiply and divide.

EXAMPLE

a Given that 3 × 7 = 21, find

  i 0.3 × 700   **ii** 210 ÷ 0.7

b Calculate

  i 3.1 × 0.6   **ii** 45 ÷ 0.3   **iii** 0.015 ÷ 0.05

a i 0.3 = 3 ÷ 10   and 700 = 7 × 100
So 0.3 × 700 = 21 ÷ 10 × 100 = 210

ii 210 = 21 × 10   and 0.7 = 7 ÷ 10
So 210 ÷ 0.7 = 3 × 10 × 10 = 300

b i 31
  ×6
 186

> Check the answer is sensible. 0.6 is a bit more than "half", and half of 3 is 1.5. This answer is a bit bigger than 1.5 ✓

So 3.**1** × 0.**6** = 1.**86**   Count how many digits are after the decimal points. There should be the same number of digits after the decimal point in the answer as in the calculation.

ii 45 ÷ 0.**3** = 450 ÷ **3** = 150

> The point moves right 1 place in each number.

Move the decimal point in **both** numbers until the number **dividing** is a whole number.

iii 0.015 ÷ 0.**05** = 1.5 ÷ **5** $\begin{array}{r} 0.3 \\ 5\overline{)1.5} \end{array}$

> The point in the answer is **above** the point in the question.

0.015 ÷ 0.05 = 0.3

Exercise BN1

1 Calculate

    a 12.3 + 1.6   **b** 10.7 − 3.6   **c** 2.4 + 1.39 + 0.97

    d 8 − 1.9   **e** 14 + 1.2   **f** 7.3 − 2.66

    g 2.7 + 0.36 − 1.8   **h** 4.2 − 1.04 + 7   **i** 2.08 + 32 − 0.82

2 Calculate

    a 12.3 × 4   **b** 2.7 × 5   **c** 9.04 ÷ 2

    d 1.25 × 0.5   **e** 4.4 ÷ 0.2   **f** 12.64 ÷ 0.4

    g 13 × 1.2   **h** 240 ÷ 0.6   **i** 121 ÷ 1.1

    j 68.7 ÷ 0.3   **k** 7.4 × 0.04   **l** 3.8 × 2.1

3 15 × 18 = 270.

    Use this fact to work out each answer.

    a 1.5 × 1.8   **b** 27 ÷ 18   **c** 1.5 × 18

    d 270 ÷ 18   **e** 2700 ÷ 18

4 Ian's car will travel an average of 35 miles on one gallon of fuel.

    How far will it travel on 0.4 gallons of fuel?

5 A serving of cereal contains 3.1 milligrams of iron.

    Rhoda has one serving of cereal a day.

    How many milligrams of iron does

    she get from this cereal in a week?

6 Hamid writes down the number of kilometres he drives each day.

Mon	Tue	Wed	Thu	Fri	Sat	Sun
25	4.6	13.8	102.6	58.9	16.6	48.1

    a How many km did he drive in the week?

    b How many km longer is his longest drive than his shortest drive?

    c On Wednesday he made three short drives.

       On average, how long was each drive?

7 This pentagon has every side the same length.

    The distance all around it is 28.5 cm.

    How long is one side?

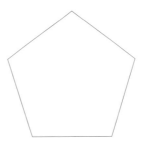

Not to scale

8 Ethan's electricity bill is £36.80.

    Each unit of electricity costs £0.80.

    How many units did Ethan use?

UNIT B

Rounding and estimation

Rounding and estimation are important mathematical skills for use in real life.

- To round correct to **significant figures**:
  1. Look at the left digit of a number.   4.386
  2. If this is **not 0** it is the first significant figure (sf)
  3. The next digit is the second and so on.   4.386
  4. To round to 2 sf, look at the 3rd significant figure: 4.386
  5. If it is 5 or more, round up: 4.**4**

> For 0.**2**005,
> the first significant figure is 2 and the second is 0.
> 0.2005 rounded to 2 sf is 0.20

- You can **estimate** answers to decimal calculations like $14.82 \div 2.97$:
  1. Round the numbers to 1 significant figure or a sensible number **in your head**. $14.82 \div 2.97 \approx 15 \div 3$
  2. Work out the answer, writing down what you do. $= 5$

> Round your answers sensibly:
> ✓ 215 109 spectators is not a good headline, 200 000 is more sensible.
> ✓ £3.1397 is not a price you could pay so round to £3.14.
> ✓ 5.8106 mm could not be measured so round to 5.8 or 6 mm.

- You can also **check** answers to problems that have already been worked out, using one of these techniques:
  1. Work the problem out backwards using **inverse operations**.
  2. Work out the problem using simple, round numbers.
  3. Just check that the answer is sensible.

> **← LOOK BACK**
> See topic AN2 on page 4 to further revise rounding.

EXAMPLE

1. Find the answers that are clearly wrong.
   a. $12.39 \div 5.82 = 6.57$
   b. $2.186 + 15.3 = 17.486$
   c. $\dfrac{5.18^2}{1.2 + 3.9} = 26.26$

2. Check these calculations.
   a. $21.6 \div 3 = 7.2$
   b. $\sqrt{8.1} = 0.9$

3. Estimate
   a. $\dfrac{6.1}{\sqrt{15.09} - 1.27^2}$
   b. $\sqrt{150} \times 3.206^2$

---

1. a. This is roughly $12 \div 6 = 2$ so 6.57 ✗
   b. This is roughly $2 + 15 = 17$ so 17.486 is probably ✓
   c. This is roughly $\dfrac{5^2}{1 + 4} = \dfrac{25}{5} = 5$ so 26.26 ✗

2. a. The opposite calculation is $7.2 \times 3 = 21.6$ ✓
   b. The opposite is 0.9^2 or $0.9 \times 0.9 = 0.81$ ✗ (9 × 9 with 2 decimal places put in)

3. a. This is roughly $\dfrac{6}{\sqrt{16} - 1^2} = \dfrac{6}{4 - 1} \approx 2$
   b. This is roughly $\sqrt{144} \times 3^2 = 12 \times 9 \approx 108$

Barry measured the part of his garden he would use for a lawn to see how much turf he would need.

Length = 12.24 m, width = 5.13 m.

He worked out the area.

Area = 12.24 x 5.13 = 62.7912 m²

Is Barry's working sensible?

A sensible answer would be 63 m².
Any turf would be supplied "to the nearest metre" so 63 would allow a little extra.

If he rounded the measurements down he would get 12 × 5 = 60 m² which would not be enough.

Exercise BN2

MEDIUM

A calculator must not be used.

1 Find the answers that are clearly wrong and show your working.
   a $12.38 - 1.7 = 12.26$
   b $9.25 \times 2.1 = 19.425$
   c $16.2 + 9.09 - 4 = 10.67$
   d $1.2^2 = 14.4$
   e $\sqrt{1.69} = 1.3$
   f $10.46 \times 2.1 - 13.45 = 8.516$

2 Round each number to the required number of significant figures.
   a 13.275 (3 sf)
   b 0.0149 (1 sf)
   c 5.0067 (3 sf)
   d $102\,364.022$ (3 sf)
   e 0.30045 (2 sf)
   f 9.09289 (2 sf)

3 Show how you can check these calculations.
   a $15.3 - 2.7 = 12.6$
   b $71.3 + 5.12 = 76.42$
   c $0.25 \times 5 = 1.25$
   d $20.5 \div 5 = 4.1$
   e $(4.03 + 1.97) \div 6 = 1$
   f $3.2 \times 1.5 - 2.2 = 2.6$

4 Work out an approximate answer to each calculation and show your working.
   a $13.78 \div 2.33$
   b 45.7×11.3
   c $15.823 - 3.71$
   d $(106.3 + 4.9) \div 11.3$
   e $5.6 \times \sqrt{17.1}$
   f $11.78^2 - 14.2$
   g $\dfrac{5.8^2 + 3.08}{\sqrt{10.2} - 0.67^2}$
   h $\left(\dfrac{9.42}{0.11}\right)^2$
   i 3.142×8.99^2

5 Sally pays £0.245 for each unit of electricity.
In a month she uses 108 units of electricity.
Work out an estimate of how much Sally's electricity bill will be for the month.
Don't forget to add VAT at 5%.

6 Carpet Direct sell carpet cut from rolls that are 4 m wide.
They will cut carpet lengths that are either whole or half metres.
The carpet costs £16.79 a square metre.

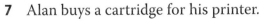

Nada's room measures 5.25 m long and 4.11m wide.
Calculate an estimate of the cost of the carpet she will need.

7 Alan buys a cartridge for his printer.
It costs £11.58 and will print 420 pages.
Calculate an estimate of the cost of printing a single page.

8 Given that $1.2 \div 0.03 = 40$, calculate:
   a $12 \div 0.3$
   b 40×0.03
   c $12 \div 400$
   d 0.04×0.3

Calculating with fractions

- To find the decimal equivalent of a fraction, divide the top number by the bottom number.

$$\frac{5}{8} = 5 \div 8 = 0.625 \qquad \frac{1}{3} = 1 \div 3 = 0.3333... \text{ (or 0.33 to 2 dp)}$$

$$\begin{array}{r} 0.625 \\ 8\overline{)5.000} \end{array}$$

$$\begin{array}{r} 0.3333 \\ 3\overline{)1.0000} \end{array}$$

You can use fractions to find proportions of amounts.

EXAMPLE

a Find $\frac{5}{8}$ of 20 m.　　b What fraction is 40 cm of 1 m?

a $20 \div 8 = 2.5$　　(divide the amount (20 m) by 8 to find **one** eight)

$2.5 \times 5 = 12.5$ m (multiply the answer by 5)

b $\frac{40}{100} = \frac{2}{5}$

If the amounts have units make sure they are the same.
Here 100 cm = 1 m

You can add and subtract fractions, but check that the denominators are the same – if they are not, change to equivalent fractions.

EXAMPLE

Calculate

a $\frac{5}{12} + \frac{11}{12}$　　b $\frac{7}{8} - \frac{3}{8}$　　c $\frac{5}{6} + \frac{5}{12}$

a $\frac{5}{12} + \frac{11}{12} = \frac{16}{12}$　　b $\frac{7}{8} - \frac{3}{8} = \frac{4}{8} = \frac{1}{2}$　　c $\frac{5}{6} + \frac{5}{12} = \frac{10}{12} + \frac{5}{12}$

$= 1\frac{4}{12} = 1\frac{1}{3}$　　　　　　　　　　$= \frac{15}{12} = 1\frac{3}{12} = 1\frac{1}{4}$

You should also know how to multiply and divide fractions.

Write the **integer** as a fraction.

EXAMPLE

Calculate

a $\frac{5}{6} \times 3$　　b $\frac{5}{7} \times \frac{2}{3}$　　c $\frac{5}{6} \div 3$　　d $\frac{5}{7} \div \frac{2}{3}$

Multiply both the tops and bottoms.

a $\frac{5}{6} \times 3 = \frac{5}{6} \times \frac{3}{1} = \frac{15}{6} = 2\frac{1}{2}$　　b $\frac{5}{7} \times \frac{2}{3} = \frac{10}{21}$

If the answer is an **improper fraction**, change to a **mixed number**.

c $\frac{5}{6} \div 3 = \frac{5}{6} \div \frac{3}{1} = \frac{5}{6} \times \frac{1}{3} = \frac{5}{18}$　　d $\frac{5}{7} \div \frac{2}{3} = \frac{5}{7} \times \frac{3}{2} = \frac{15}{14} = 1\frac{1}{14}$

Invert the second fraction and change the ÷ to a ×.

The reciprocal of 6 = $\frac{1}{6}$.

- The reciprocal of a number is "1 over the number" or "the fraction turned upside down".

The reciprocal of $\frac{2}{3} = \frac{3}{2}$.

Exercise BN3

A calculator must not be used.

1 Calculate

   a $\frac{1}{4}$ of £24   **b** $\frac{3}{4}$ of 30 m   **c** $\frac{2}{3}$ of 15 km   **d** $\frac{5}{8}$ of 64 g

   e $\frac{3}{5}$ of £12   **f** $\frac{4}{5}$ of 21 km   **g** $\frac{2}{3}$ of £11.40   **h** $\frac{2}{9}$ of 18.09 m

2 Write the first quantity as a fraction of the second.
Give each answer in its simplest possible form.

   a 10 cm of 2 m   **b** 35p of £2

   c 1 day out of January   **d** 50 g of 1 kg

3 Calculate

   a $\frac{1}{4}+\frac{1}{4}$ $\frac{2}{4}$ **b** $\frac{1}{4}\times\frac{1}{4}$ **c** $\frac{1}{4}\div\frac{1}{4}$ **d** $\frac{3}{4}-\frac{1}{2}$

   e $\frac{3}{8}+\frac{1}{2}$ **f** $\frac{2}{3}+\frac{1}{5}$ **g** $\frac{3}{5}\times 6$ **h** $\frac{2}{7}\div\frac{4}{5}$

   i $\frac{5}{8}\times\frac{6}{11}$ **j** $10\times\frac{1}{4}$ **k** $\frac{5}{8}\div\frac{1}{4}$ **l** $\frac{4}{5}\div 5$

4 Change each of these fractions to a decimal.
If a decimal is recurring, round it correct to 2 dp.

   a $\frac{3}{4}$ **b** $\frac{2}{5}$ **c** $\frac{3}{8}$

   d $\frac{5}{9}$ **e** $\frac{3}{11}$ **f** $\frac{3}{20}$

5 **a** Write down the reciprocal of 8 as a fraction.

   b Multiply your answer to **a** by 8.

   c What always happens when you multiply a number by its reciprocal?

6 $\frac{2}{3}$ of people on a ride were under 15 years old.

   $\frac{1}{9}$ of the people were 15 to 19 years old.

   What fraction of the people on the ride were over 19 years old?

7 Which of these is the **exact** answer to $\frac{2}{3}$ of £10? Show your working.

   a £6.66   **b** £6$\frac{1}{3}$ **c** £6.$\dot{6}$

8 It costs £24 to run a battery-powered car for 7 days.
Here are two statements:

> **1** The average cost to run the car for a day is £3.42.
>
> **2** The average cost to run the car for a day is £3$\frac{3}{7}$.

Give one reason why **each** statement could be a good answer to the question.

• **Terminating decimals** have a fixed number of digits.

You can write a terminating decimal as a fraction:

1 Find the value of the column containing the last decimal digit.
2 This is the denominator of the fraction.
3 Write the fraction with the decimal digits (after the decimal point) as the numerator. $0.12 = \dfrac{12}{100}$
4 Cancel your fraction where possible. $= \dfrac{3}{25}$

0.12 and 1.255 and 3.3333 are terminating decimals.

U	.	$\dfrac{1}{10}$	$\dfrac{1}{100}$	$\dfrac{1}{1000}$	$\dfrac{1}{10000}$
0	.	1	2		

EXAMPLE

Convert each decimal to a fraction in its simplest form.
a 0.8   b 2.28   c 10.505

a $0.8 = \dfrac{8}{10} = \dfrac{4}{5}$ b $2.28 = 2\dfrac{28}{100} = \dfrac{7}{25}$

c $10.505 = 10\dfrac{505}{1000} = 10\dfrac{101}{200}$

If the denominator of a fraction has prime factors of 2 and 5, the fraction will convert to a terminating decimal.
If its prime factors are anything other than 2 and 5, then it will convert to a recurring decimal.

EXAMINER'S TIP

Always remember to cancel.

• **Recurring decimals** have digits that repeat forever in a pattern.
Any digits that repeat are written with a dot over them.

$0.\dot{2}$ repeats as 0.2222.....
$0.\dot{1}24\dot{5}$ repeats as 0.12451245...

These common fractions are recurring decimals:

$\dfrac{1}{3} = 0.\dot{3}$ $\dfrac{1}{6} = 0.1\dot{6}$ $\dfrac{1}{11} = 0.\dot{0}\dot{9}$

To convert a recurring decimal to a fraction:

1. Write an equation with the decimal equal to *n*. $n = 0.166\,666...$
2. Multiply the decimal by a power of 10. $10n = 1.666\,666...$
3. Subtract the smaller from the larger decimal. $9n = 1.5$
4. Divide the answer by the number of *n*. $n = \dfrac{1.5}{9}$
5. If the numerator is not a whole number, multiply top and bottom by a power of 10 so that both are whole. $n = \dfrac{15}{90}$
6. Cancel. $n = \dfrac{1}{6}$

When **all** digits repeat after the decimal point, you can use this trick:

• Count from the last digit that repeats to the decimal point $0.\dot{0}\dot{9}$
• Write all these digits over the same number of 9s $\dfrac{09}{99}$
• Cancel. $\dfrac{1}{11}$

Convert each recurring decimal to a fraction in its simplest form.

a $0.1\dot{5}$ **b** $2.3\dot{5}$

---

a Use the trick: $\dfrac{15}{99} = \dfrac{5}{33}$

b $n = 2.3\dot{5}$

$10n = 23.\dot{5}$

$9n = 21.2$

$n = \dfrac{21.2}{9} = \dfrac{212}{90} = 2\dfrac{32}{90} = 2\dfrac{16}{45}$

Exercise BN4

MEDIUM   A calculator must not be used.

1 Write each of these decimals as a fraction.

   a 0.3   **b** 0.03   **c** 1.27   **d** 11.09   **e** 6.101

2 Write each of these decimals as a fraction in its simplest form.

   a 0.4   **b** 0.05   **c** 1.25   **d** 11.56   **e** 6.125

   f 12.55   **g** 1.405   **h** 6.508   **i** 0.015   **j** 21.006

3 Which of these decimals are recurring and which are terminating?

If a decimal is recurring, write out the first six digits after the decimal point.

If a decimal is terminating, write it as a fraction.

   a 0.111   **b** $0.\dot{1}0\dot{1}$ **c** $0.502\dot{7}$ **d** 1.2158

4 Elena buys six different scarves and she pays €58.

She finds the average price by calculating

    €58 ÷ 6 = €9.666666666....

Explain why this is not an exact price.

5 Callum works out $25 ÷ 3 = 8.\dot{3}$.

He checks this by doing 8.3 × 3.

   a What answer does he get?

   b Does this mean that Callum got the wrong answer to 25 ÷ 3?

6 Convert each recurring decimal to a fraction in its simplest form.

   a $0.\dot{5}$ **b** $0.1\dot{5}$ **c** $0.\dot{4}$ **d** $0.\dot{5}1\dot{3}$

   e $1.5\dot{6}$ **f** $1.0\dot{5}$ **g** $2.2\dot{1}$ **h** $0.02\dot{6}$

7 Write each of these fractions as a recurring decimal.

   a $\dfrac{5}{9}$ **b** $\dfrac{1}{7}$ **c** $\dfrac{1}{90}$ **d** $\dfrac{2}{11}$

Fractions and decimals

These headings give the **place value** of a **digit** in a number.

10 000	1000	100	10	1	.	$\dfrac{1}{10}$	$\dfrac{1}{100}$

- The **digit** that is furthest **left** has the biggest value.

  320.3 is bigger than **5**9.96

  0.**1** is bigger than 0.0**9**04

> **3** hundred is bigger than **5** tens (fifty).
>
> **1** tenth is bigger than **9** hundredths.

EXAMPLE

Write these numbers in order, starting with the smallest.

12.2   20   1.99   0.909   43.01

. . . .

0.**9**09   **1**.99   **1**2.2   **2**0   **4**3.01

- You can compare fractions by writing them as **equivalent fractions** with the same denominator.

EXAMPLE

a Which fraction is bigger:

$\dfrac{2}{3}$ or $\dfrac{3}{4}$?

b Write these fractions in ascending order.

$\dfrac{2}{5}$ $\dfrac{3}{4}$ $\dfrac{7}{10}$ $\dfrac{1}{2}$

. . . .

a $\dfrac{2}{3} \times \dfrac{4}{4} = \dfrac{8}{12}$ and $\dfrac{3}{4} \times \dfrac{3}{3} = \dfrac{9}{12}$

> Multiply top and bottom of each fraction by the same number so that they each have the same denominator.

$\dfrac{9}{12}$ is bigger than $\dfrac{8}{12}$ so $\dfrac{3}{4}$ is bigger than $\dfrac{2}{3}$

b $\dfrac{2}{5} \times \dfrac{4}{4} = \dfrac{8}{20}$ $\dfrac{3}{4} \times \dfrac{5}{5} = \dfrac{15}{20}$ $\dfrac{7}{10} \times \dfrac{2}{2} = \dfrac{14}{20}$ $\dfrac{1}{2} \times \dfrac{10}{10} = \dfrac{10}{20}$

So in ascending order: $\dfrac{2}{5}$ $\dfrac{1}{2}$ $\dfrac{7}{10}$ $\dfrac{3}{4}$

- You can write a fraction in its **simplest form** by **cancelling**.

EXAMPLE

Cancel each fraction to its simplest form.

a $\dfrac{18}{24}$ **b** $3\dfrac{24}{36}$

> You could divide first by 2 $\left(=\dfrac{9}{12}\right)$ and then divide by 3.
>
> **Always** check there are no more common factors.

. . . .

a $\dfrac{18}{24} = \dfrac{3}{4}$ Divide top and bottom by 6

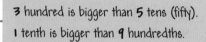

b $3\dfrac{24}{36} = 3\dfrac{2}{3}$

> Divide top and bottom of the fraction by 12.
>
> You could divide in steps by using 2, 3, 4 or 6, but don't leave the answer as $3\dfrac{12}{18}$ as this is not the simplest form.

Exercise BN5

MEDIUM

1 Copy and complete these equivalent fractions.

a $\dfrac{3}{4} = \dfrac{}{8} = \dfrac{12}{} = \dfrac{}{60}$

b $\dfrac{5}{6} = \dfrac{15}{} = \dfrac{}{30} = \dfrac{75}{}$

A calculator must not be used.

2 Cancel each fraction to its simplest form.

a $\dfrac{4}{12}$ b $\dfrac{6}{10}$ c $\dfrac{3}{36}$ d $\dfrac{8}{14}$ e $\dfrac{9}{18}$ f $\dfrac{7}{28}$

g $\dfrac{16}{36}$ h $\dfrac{240}{360}$ i $\dfrac{12}{30}$ j $\dfrac{15}{50}$ k $\dfrac{40}{100}$ l $\dfrac{20}{48}$

3 Put each set of numbers in order, starting with the smallest.

a 102, 97.8, 100.9

b 21.9, 2.19, 219, 0.219

c 0.3, 0.29, 0.18, 0.1

d 6.07, 6.17, 6.04, 6.18

e 9, 9.1, 8.9, 9.11

f 3.8, 3.08, 3.79, 3

4 Put each set of fractions in order, starting with the smallest.

a $\dfrac{3}{4}, \dfrac{1}{2}, \dfrac{1}{4}$

b $\dfrac{2}{3}, \dfrac{5}{12}, \dfrac{5}{6}$

c $\dfrac{3}{10}, \dfrac{4}{5}, \dfrac{13}{20}$

d $\dfrac{7}{12}, \dfrac{1}{6}, \dfrac{3}{4}$

e $\dfrac{2}{3}, \dfrac{7}{9}, \dfrac{13}{18}$

f $\dfrac{3}{5}, \dfrac{7}{10}, \dfrac{1}{2}, \dfrac{13}{20}$

5 In January Bill spent $\dfrac{3}{5}$ of his income.

In February he spent $\dfrac{5}{12}$ of his income.

In which month did Bill spend the larger fraction of his income?

6 Two shipments of glass vases were sent.
In one shipment 19 out of the 150 vases were damaged.
In the second shipment, 7 out of the 50 vases were broken.
In which shipment was the fraction of broken vases greater?

7 Two breakfast cereals show the following information on their labels.

Cereal A

Protein	13 g
Carbohydrate	77 g
Fibre	3 g
Other	7 g
Total weight	100 g

Cereal B

Protein	4 g
Carbohydrate	23 g
Fibre	1 g
Other	2 g
Total weight	30 g

a Work out the fraction of carbohydrate in each cereal.

b Which cereal has the greater fraction of fibre?

Percentages, fractions and decimals BN6

- A **percentage** is a fraction with a denominator of 100.

  36% means $\dfrac{36}{100}$

$\dfrac{36}{100}$ cancels to $\dfrac{9}{25}$.

So 36% = $\dfrac{9}{25}$

You can also convert between percentages and decimals.

$70\% = 70 \div 100 = 0.7$ $0.35 = 0.35 \times 100\% = 35\%$

You must learn the relationships shown in the tables below.
You can work out other facts from them.

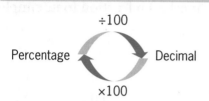

÷100

Percentage ⇄ Decimal

×100

Fraction	Decimal	Percentage
$\dfrac{1}{2}$	0.5	50%
$\dfrac{1}{4}$	0.25	25%
$\dfrac{3}{4}$	0.75	75%

Fraction	Decimal	Percentage
$\dfrac{1}{3}$	$0.\dot{3}$	$33.\dot{3}\%$
$\dfrac{1}{5}$	0.2	20%
$\dfrac{1}{10}$	0.1	10%

$\dfrac{2}{3}$ is twice $\dfrac{1}{3}$
so $\dfrac{2}{3}$ is 33.3% × 2
= 66.6%

So $\dfrac{3}{10}$ = 0.3
= 30%

EXAMPLE

a Put these quantities in order of size, starting with the smallest.

0.28, $\dfrac{1}{4}$, 26%

b Complete this table.

Fraction	Decimal	Percentage
		20%
	0.07	
$\dfrac{3}{5}$		60%

a $0.28 \times 100 = 28\%$ $\dfrac{1}{4} = 25\%$

The order is 25%, 26%, 28%

or $\dfrac{1}{4}$, 26%, 0.28

b

Fraction	Decimal	Percentage
$\dfrac{1}{5}$	0.2	20%
$\dfrac{7}{100}$	0.07	7%
$\dfrac{3}{5}$	0.6	60%

EXAMINER'S TIP:

Change a percentage to a decimal by dividing it by 100.

7% means $\dfrac{7}{100}$ or
$7 \div 100 = 0.07$

Percentages are often used in money contexts.

EXAMPLE

a Find 35% of £26.

b Jayne saves £27 when she buys a dress in a sale.
Jayne paid £63 for the dress.
What percentage was the dress reduced by?

a 10% of £26 = 26 ÷ 10 = £2.60
30% of £26 = £2.60 × 3 = £7.80
5% of £26 = £2.60 ÷ 2 = £1.30
So 35% = 30% + 5% = £7.80 + £1.30 = £9.10

b $\dfrac{27}{90} = \dfrac{3}{10} = \dfrac{30}{100} = 30\%$

The dress used to cost 63 + 27 = £90.

Cancel by 9 and then $\dfrac{3}{10} \times \dfrac{10}{10} = \dfrac{30}{100}$ or 30%

Exercise BN6

A calculator must not be used.

1 Write each set of numbers in order, starting with the smallest.

    a $45\%, \frac{1}{2}, 0.35$ **b** $0.07, \frac{4}{5}, 70\%$ **c** $\frac{3}{4}, 69\%, 0.8$ **d** $68\%, \frac{2}{3}, 0.7$

2 Which of $\frac{2}{5}$ or 0.52 is the larger?
    Show how you decide.

3 Celine scores 28 out of 40 in her test. Damien scores 69%.
    Who has the best score?
    Show how you decide.

4 Xi wants to find 35% of £85.
    Should he multiply by 3.5, $\frac{3}{5}$, 0.35 or $\frac{35}{10}$?
    Show how you decide.

5 Calculate
    a   40% of 78 metres   **b**   25% of 88 men   **c**   10% of £5
    d   60% of £12   **e**   15% of 64 g   **f**   1% of 7800
    g   35% of 80 km   **h**   55% of £840   **i**   6% of 95 cm
    j   125% of £44   **k**   45% of 12 metres   **l**   21% of 2000

6 John has worked out 19% of £460 as £8.47.
    Explain whether John is correct or not.

7 Carole buys a savings bond for £2200. She will get 5% interest
    paid at the end of the year.
    Ian buys his bond for £1500 and gets 7.5% interest paid at
    the end of the year.
    Who gets the most interest and by how much?

8 $\frac{1}{2}$ is the same as 50%.
    Show how you can use this fact to write $\frac{7}{8}$ as a percentage.

9 Copy and complete this table.

Fraction	Decimal	Percentage
	0.01	
		70%
$\frac{2}{5}$		

10 Dan has £480. He wants to earn interest of at least £24 on this money in a year.
    What is the lowest rate of interest he can invest the money at?

The area of a square is $l \times l$ or l^2
(you say: "l **squared**")

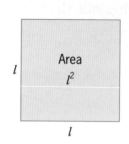

If $l = 6$ cm
Then area $l^2 = 6^2 = 6 \times 6 = 36$ cm^2
36 is the **square** of 6

These are **square numbers** (they are the answers to 1×1, 2×2, 3×3, …, 15×15):

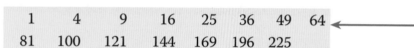

1	4	9	16	25	36	49	64
81	100	121	144	169	196	225	

You should learn all these numbers.

One side of a square is the
square root of the area.
$$l = \sqrt{\text{area}}$$

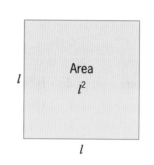

If area $l^2 = 49$ cm^2
then one side $l = \sqrt{49} = 7$ cm.
7 is the **square root** of 49.

- A square root has two values, one positive and one
  negative.
  $\sqrt{25} = 5$ and -5 because both $5 \times 5 = 25$ and $-5 \times -5 = 25$
  5 is the positive square root of 25 and -5 is the negative
  square root of 25.

The volume of a cube is $l \times l \times l$ or l^3
(you say: "l **cubed**")

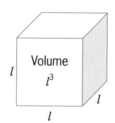

If $l = 4$ cm
Then volume $l^3 = 4^3 = 64$ cm^3.
64 is the **cube** of 4.

These are **cube numbers** (these are the answers to $1 \times 1 \times 1$, $2 \times 2 \times 2$, …):

1 8 27 64 125 216 343 512 729 1000

You should learn all these numbers.

One edge of a cube is the **cube root**
of the volume.
$$l = \sqrt[3]{\text{volume}}$$

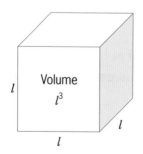

If volume $l^3 = 125$ cm^3
then one edge $l = \sqrt[3]{125} = 5$ cm.
5 is the **cube root** of 125.

a Look at this list of numbers.

3   8   25   40   64   80

From the list, write   **i** a square number

ii a number that is both a square number and a cube number.

b Write down   **i** the cube of 5

ii the negative square root of 100.

a i   25   **ii** 64
b i 125   **ii** −10

EXAMINER'S TIP

$\sqrt{100} = 10$.

Just write − in front of 10.

Exercise BN7

MEDIUM

A calculator must not be used.

1 Look at this list of numbers.

1   5   12   17   25   48   91   125   169

Write down

a a cube number that is also a square number

b a square number bigger than 30

c the biggest square number minus the smallest cube number.

2 Work out the value of
    a the cube of 4   **b** the square root of 169
    c 12 squared   **d** 20 squared
    e $3^2 + 2^2$ **f** $3^2 - 3^2$
    g $5^3 + 2^3$ **h** $\sqrt{100}$
    i 14^2 **j** 3 cubed − 2 squared.

3 Without a calculator, write the whole number that is closest in value to
    a $\sqrt{50}$ **b** $\sqrt{80}$
    c $\sqrt{30}$ **d** $\sqrt{40}$
    e $\sqrt{120}$ **f** $\sqrt{150}$
    g $\sqrt{8}$ **h** $\sqrt{5}$

4 The area of a square is 400 cm².
    a How long is one of its sides?
    b What is its perimeter?

5 A wire frame is made in the shape of a cube.
The frame surrounds 1000 cm³ of air.
What length of wire is used to make the frame?

UNIT B

You can write repeated multiplications using **indices**, or **powers**.

$12 \times 12 \times 12 = 12^3$ $5 \times 5 \times 5 \times 5 = 5^4$

The **base** is 12   The **power** is 3

The index, or power, tells you how many of the base numbers to multiply together.

> 1 index, 2 indices.

> If the index is 2, this is called "squared".
> $5^2 = 5$ squared
> If the index is 3, this is called "cubed".
> $7^3 = 7$ cubed

- When the base number n is the same,
  - you multiply by **adding the indices** $n^a \times n^b = n^{a+b}$
  - you divide by **subtracting the indices** $n^a \div n^b = n^{a-b}$

- There are some special cases of indices that you should know.
  If the index is zero, the answer is always 1.
  $$n^0 = 1 \text{ so } 5^0 = 1 = (-7)^0 = 456^0 = 1 \ldots$$
  If the index is raised to a second index, you multiply the two indices.
  $$(n^a)^b = n^{ab} \qquad (2^3)^2 = 2^6 = 64$$

  > $2 \times 2 \times 2 \times 2 \times 2 \times 2 = 64$

  If the index is negative, the answer is usually a fraction.
  $$n^{-a} = \frac{1}{n^a} \qquad 2^{-3} = \frac{1}{2^3}\left(=\frac{1}{8}\right)$$
  If the index is a unit fraction, then the answer is a root.
  $$n^{\frac{1}{a}} = \sqrt[a]{n} \qquad 9^{\frac{1}{2}} = 3 \qquad 32^{\frac{1}{5}} = \sqrt[5]{32} = 2$$

  > In particular,
  > $n^{\frac{1}{2}} = \sqrt{n}$
  > $n^{\frac{1}{3}} = \sqrt[3]{n}$

  If the index is a fraction, the answer is always a root raised to a power.
  $$n^{\frac{b}{a}} = \left(\sqrt[a]{n}\right)^b \qquad 27^{\frac{2}{3}} = \left(\sqrt[3]{27}\right)^2 = 3^2 = 9$$

EXAMPLE

1 Find the value of each of the following.

   a $\left(\dfrac{1}{2}\right)^3$ **b** 2^5 **c** 8^{-2} **d** $\dfrac{4^3}{2^5}$ **e** $81^{\frac{3}{4}}$

2 Simplify each of the following, writing your answer as an index.

   a $4^2 \times 4^3$ **b** $3^3 \times 3^{-5}$ **c** $4^3 \div 2^3$

   d $\dfrac{7^2 \times 7^3}{7^4}$ **e** $3^5 \times 2^3 \times 3^3 \times 2$ **f** $\left(7^2\right)^3$

---

1 a $\left(\dfrac{1}{2}\right)^3 = \dfrac{1}{2} \times \dfrac{1}{2} \times \dfrac{1}{2} = \dfrac{1}{8}$ **b** $2^5 = 2 \times 2 \times 2 \times 2 \times 2 = 32$

  c $8^{-2} = \dfrac{1}{8^2} = \dfrac{1}{64}$ **d** $\dfrac{4^3}{2^5} = \dfrac{4 \times 4 \times 4}{2 \times 2 \times 2 \times 2 \times 2} = \dfrac{64}{32} = 2$

  e $81^{\frac{3}{4}} = \left(\sqrt[4]{81}\right)^3 = 3^3 = 27$

2 a 4^5 **b** 3^{-2} **c** 2^3 **d** 7 **e** $3^8 \times 2^4$ **f** 7^6

Exercise BN8

MEDIUM

A calculator must not be used.

1 Write each of these using indices.

  a $2 \times 2 \times 2 \times 2 \times 2 \times 2$ **b** $3 \times 3 \times 3$ **c** $5 \times 5 \times 5 \times 5 \times 5$

  d $3 \times 2 \times 3 \times 2 \times 3 \times 3$ **e** $5 \times 6 \times 6 \times 6 \times 6 \times 5$ **f** $10 \times 10 \times 3 \times 3 \times 10$

2 Write each of these as a multiplication of single digits.
(Do not do the multiplication.)

  a 4^3 **b** 5^4 **c** $3^3 \times 2^5$ **d** $4^3 \times 5^3$ **e** $3^2 \times 7^4$

3 Find the value of each of these quantities.

  a 10^{-3} **b** $\left(400^{\frac{1}{2}}\right)^3$ **c** 1^{12} **d** $\left(\frac{4}{9}\right)^{\frac{1}{2}}$

  e $4^{\frac{1}{2}} \times 2^2$ **f** $16^{\frac{3}{4}} \div 4$ **g** $8^{\frac{1}{3}} + 10^{-2}$ **h** $\frac{6^2}{3^2}$

4 Simplify each of these, leaving your answer as a number with an index.

  a $2^3 \times 2^4 \times 2^2$ **b** $5^3 \times 5^3 \times 5^3$ **c** $4^{12} \div 4^3$

  d $3^{0.5} \times 3^{0.75}$ **e** $\left(\frac{1}{3}\right)^3 \div \left(\frac{1}{3}\right)^{\frac{1}{2}}$ **f** $(5^3 \times 5^2)^2 \div 5^3$

  g $\frac{10^3 \times 10^2}{10^4}$ **h** $4^3 \times 3^4 \times 4^2 \times 3^2$ **i** $7 \times 4^2 \times 7^5 \times 4$

  j $5^3 \times 3^2 \times 5^2 \times 3$ **k** $\frac{5^3 \times 5 \times 4^3}{4^2 \times 5^{-2}}$ **l** $6^2 \times 5^3 \times 6^5 \div 5^2$

  m $3^4 \times 2^5 \div 3^4$ **n** $6^4 \div 6^3 \times 4^2 \div 6$ **o** $(7^2)^3 \times 7^3 \div 7^4$

5 Which of 0.5^4 or $\left(\frac{1}{4}\right)^3$ has the greater value?
Show your working.

6 Find a square number, n, that is less than 100 and satisfies the
equation $n = 3^a$, where a is an integer.

7 This pattern of numbers continues:
    $2, \ 2^2, \ 2^3, \ 2^4, \ 2^5, \ \dots$

  a What is the tenth number in the pattern?
    Write your answer as a power of 2.

  b Write the first six numbers in the sequence as ordinary numbers.

  c What is the answer when you add the **first**:

    i two numbers   **ii** three numbers   **iii** four numbers in the pattern?

  d Show how you can find the total of the first nine numbers in the pattern in
two different ways.

UNIT B

Here is a reminder of some of the facts on indices covered previously:

- $(n^a)^b = n^{ab}$
- $n^{\frac{1}{a}} = \sqrt[a]{n}$
- $n^{\frac{b}{a}} = (\sqrt[a]{n})^b$ This follows from the previous two facts: $n^{\frac{b}{a}} = (n^{\frac{1}{a}})^b$.
- $n^{-\frac{b}{a}} = \dfrac{1}{(\sqrt[a]{n})^b}$ This follows from the previous fact and also the fact that $n^{-a} = \dfrac{1}{n^a}$.

> See page 62 for a full list of index facts.

EXAMPLE

Simplify   **a** $\left(p^4\right)^{\frac{3}{2}}$ **b** $\left(p^4\right)^{-\frac{3}{2}}$ **c** $\left(16p^4\right)^{\frac{1}{4}}$ **d** $\left(\dfrac{a^2}{f^6}\right)^{-\frac{1}{2}}$

....

a $\left(p^4\right)^{\frac{3}{2}} = p^{4\times\frac{3}{2}} = p^6$ **b** $\left(p^4\right)^{-\frac{3}{2}} = p^{4\times-\frac{3}{2}} = p^{-6}$

c $\left(16p^4\right)^{\frac{1}{4}} = 16^{\frac{1}{4}} \times p^{4\times\frac{1}{4}} = \sqrt[4]{16} \times p = 2p$ **d** $\left(\dfrac{a^2}{f^6}\right)^{-\frac{1}{2}} = \left(\dfrac{f^6}{a^2}\right)^{\frac{1}{2}} = \dfrac{f^{6\times\frac{1}{2}}}{a^{2\times\frac{1}{2}}} = \dfrac{f^3}{a}$

- A surd is a **root** that is an **irrational number**, like $\sqrt{2}$. Surds cannot be evaluated exactly.

> **Irrational numbers** cannot be expressed accurately either as a decimal or as a fraction.

Here are some rules for working with surds.

- $\sqrt{a} \times \sqrt{b} = \sqrt{a \times b}$ • $\dfrac{\sqrt{a}}{\sqrt{b}} = \sqrt{\dfrac{a}{b}}$ • $(\sqrt{a})^2 = a$

These rules follow from the facts on indices above.
Can you work out how?
You can often simplify an expression containing surds.

EXAMPLE

1 Simplify   **a** $\sqrt{50}$ **b** $\sqrt{48} + \sqrt{27}$

2 $g = 2 + 3\sqrt{2}$ and $f = 5 - 2\sqrt{2}$. Find gf.

> Treat $\sqrt{3}$ just like a letter in algebra.
> $4a + 3a = 7a$

....

1 a $\sqrt{50} = \sqrt{25 \times 2} = \sqrt{25} \times \sqrt{2}$ **b** $\sqrt{48} + \sqrt{27} = \sqrt{16 \times 3} + \sqrt{9 \times 3}$

         $= 5\sqrt{2}$ $= 4\sqrt{3} + 3\sqrt{3}$

                                                         $= 7\sqrt{3}$

2 $gf = (2 + 3\sqrt{2})(5 - 2\sqrt{2})$
      $= 10 - 4\sqrt{2} + 15\sqrt{2} - 6\sqrt{2} \times \sqrt{2}$
      $= 10 + 11\sqrt{2} - 12 = 11\sqrt{2} - 2$

> Treat this as $(a + b)(p - q)$
> $3\sqrt{2} \times 2\sqrt{2} = 6 \times (\sqrt{2})^2 = 6 \times 2$

When surds occur in fractions as the denominator, you should
rationalise the denominator.

Rationalise   **a** $\dfrac{3}{\sqrt{3}}$ **b** $\dfrac{2\sqrt{2}}{3\sqrt{5}}$

a $\dfrac{3}{\sqrt{3}} \times \dfrac{\sqrt{3}}{\sqrt{3}} = \dfrac{3\sqrt{3}}{3} = \sqrt{3}$ **b** $\dfrac{2\sqrt{2}}{3\sqrt{5}} \times \dfrac{\sqrt{5}}{\sqrt{5}} = \dfrac{2\sqrt{10}}{3 \times \sqrt{5} \times \sqrt{5}} = \dfrac{2\sqrt{10}}{15}$

$\sqrt{3} \times \sqrt{3} = 3$

Exercise BN9

HIGH

A calculator must not be used.

1 Simplify these surds.
   a $\sqrt{3} + 5\sqrt{3}$ **b** $12\sqrt{11} \times 5$ **c** $4\sqrt{3} - 3\sqrt{3}$ **d** $\sqrt{3} \times \sqrt{3} - 2$

   e $\sqrt{13} + 6\sqrt{13} - 4\sqrt{13}$ **f** $4\sqrt{7} \times 2\sqrt{7}$ **g** $7\sqrt{15} - \sqrt{15}$ **h** $2\sqrt{8} \times 8\sqrt{2}$

2 Write each of these expressions in the form $p\sqrt{q}$, where q is the smallest possible integer.
   a $\sqrt{75}$ **b** $2\sqrt{12}$ **c** $5\sqrt{18}$ **d** $7\sqrt{200}$ **e** $\dfrac{6\sqrt{50}}{5}$

3 Simplify
   a $\sqrt{18} - 2\sqrt{2}$ **b** $3\sqrt{75} + 2\sqrt{3}$ **c** $\sqrt{32} \times \sqrt{18}$ **d** $5\sqrt{12} + 2\sqrt{75}$

4 Expand and simplify
   a $\sqrt{5}(2\sqrt{5} + 2)$ **b** $2\sqrt{7}(3 - \sqrt{7})$ **c** $4\sqrt{5}(\sqrt{80} - 2\sqrt{5})$

   d $(3 - \sqrt{2})(4 + \sqrt{2})$ **e** $(5 + \sqrt{3})(7 + \sqrt{3})$ **f** $(8 - \sqrt{7})(5 + \sqrt{7})$

   g $(5 - 2\sqrt{7})(6 + 3\sqrt{7})$ **h** $(6 + 2\sqrt{5})(5 + \sqrt{5})$ **i** $(3\sqrt{11} - 8)(\sqrt{11} + 2)$

5 Find the value of these expressions if $m = 2 + 2\sqrt{5}$ and $n = 3 - 5\sqrt{5}$.
   a $m + n$ **b** mn **c** m^2 **d** $2\sqrt{5}n$ **e** $m - 2n$

6 Rationalise the denominator and, where possible, simplify the following.
   a $\dfrac{20}{\sqrt{2}}$ **b** $\dfrac{20}{\sqrt{10}}$ **c** $\dfrac{5}{\sqrt{3}}$ **d** $\dfrac{2}{3\sqrt{2}} \times \dfrac{9}{\sqrt{3}}$ **e** $\dfrac{2\sqrt{5}}{5\sqrt{2}}$

7 Simplify
   a $\dfrac{2}{(\sqrt{2} + 3)} \times \dfrac{(\sqrt{2} - 3)}{(\sqrt{2} - 3)}$ **b** $\dfrac{3}{(5 + \sqrt{5})} \times \dfrac{(5 - \sqrt{5})}{(5 - \sqrt{5})}$

   c Use your results to help you rationalise the denominator of $\dfrac{6}{(3 - \sqrt{7})}$.

8 Simplify   **a** $\left(g^3\right)^{\frac{2}{3}}$ **b** $\left(m^6\right)^{-\frac{3}{2}}$ **c** $\left(27r^6\right)^{\frac{2}{3}}$ **d** $\left(8\dfrac{a^9}{b^6}\right)^{-\frac{1}{3}}$

Straight-line graphs

- Straight-line graphs can be written in the form $y = mx + c$, where m is the **gradient** of the line and c is the **y-intercept**.

← LOOK BACK

See topic AA1 on page 16 to revise letter symbols and the meaning of 'equation', 'formula', 'identity' and 'expression'.

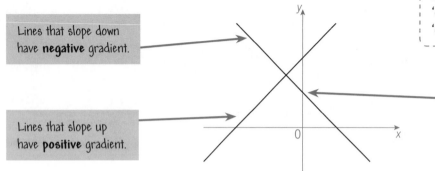

Lines that slope down have **negative** gradient.

The y-**intercept** is where the line crosses the y-axis.

Lines that slope up have **positive** gradient.

- The **gradient** of a line, m, is calculated by finding

$$\frac{\text{vertical increase}}{\text{horizontal increase}}.$$

Parallel lines have the same gradient.

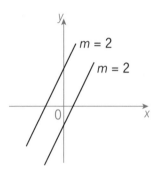

$m = 2$

$m = 2$

The gradients of **perpendicular** lines are **negative reciprocals**.

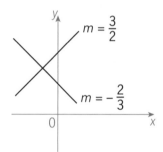

$m = \frac{3}{2}$

$m = -\frac{2}{3}$

If the vertical variable **decreases** as the horizontal variable **increases**, it is a negative vertical increase.

EXAMPLE

Find

a the gradient of the line $y = 4x + 5$

b the equation of the line parallel to $y = 4x + 5$ that passes through the point $(0, -3)$.

c the equation of the line that is perpendicular to $y = 4x + 5$ that passes through point $(0, 9)$

← LOOK BACK

See topic AA3 on page 19 to revise coordinates.

a The gradient is 4.

b The line's gradient is 4 (as it is parallel), its y-intercept is -3.

Therefore its equation is $y = 4x - 3$.

c Its gradient is $-\frac{1}{4}$ (negative reciprocal of 4), its y-intercept is 9. Therefore its equation is $y = -\frac{1}{4}x + 9$

- To solve simultaneous equations graphically, draw the straight-line graphs of both equations on the same grid.

Use a graphical method to solve $x + y = 6$
$$y = x + 1$$

Plot some points to help you draw the graphs.

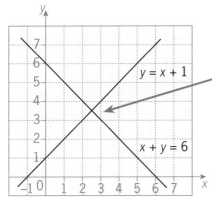

The solution is $x = 2.5$, $y = 3.5$

The graphs cross at the point (2.5, 3.5). This gives you the **solution** of the original equations.

You can check your answer by **substituting** your values into each equation and seeing if both work.

EXAMINER'S TIP

When you are using graphs to solve simultaneous equations the values may not be whole numbers.

Exercise BA1

MEDIUM

1 Draw the graph of $y = 2x + 4$ where $-4 \le x \le 3$.

2 Write down the gradient and y-intercept of each of these graphs.
   a $y = 6x - 2$ b $y = \dfrac{2}{3}x$ c $y = 8 - x$

3 a Find the gradient of the line, L, that passes through $(2, 7)$ and $(5, -2)$.
   b Line M is parallel to L and passes through $(0, 1)$. Find the equation of M.
   c Line N is perpendicular to L and passes through $(0, -4)$. Find the equation of N.

4 Two lines are perpendicular.
   What is the product of their gradients?

5 Use the diagram to solve these pairs of simultaneous equations. Give your answers correct to 1 decimal place.
   a $x + 2y = 10$ b $x + 2y = 10$
       $y = 5x + 3$ $2y - x = 3$
   c $2y - x = 3$
       $y = 5x + 3$

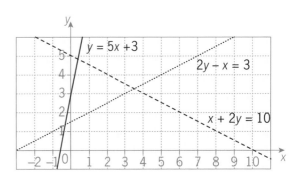

6 Use a graphical method to solve $2x + 3y = 12$
$$y = 2x + 1$$

7 The lines $2x + 5y = 36$ and $7x + ky = 15$ cross at the point where $x = 3$. Find the value of k.

8 Try to solve these simultaneous equations algebraically:
   $3x + 4y = 7$
   $9x + 12y = 10$
   What does your solution tell you about the graphs of
   $3x + 4y = 7$ and
   $9x + 12y = 10$?

Real-life linear functions

- A **linear function** can be represented with a straight-line graph.
- A linear function of x and y can be written in the form $y = mx + c$. This is the **equation** of its straight line.

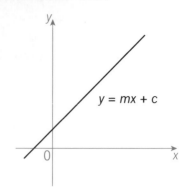

Some real-life situations can be modelled with linear functions.

EXAMPLE

The striped ground-cricket makes a fast chirping sound.
Scientists measured the number of chirps (N) the striped ground-cricket made each second and the temperature (T) in °C.

a Plot these values on a graph, and draw a **line of best fit** through your points.
b Find an equation connecting N and T.
c How many chirps would you expect to hear per second if the temperature was 30°C?
d Why would it not be sensible to use your equation to find the number of chirps made at 10°C?

T	N
31.4	20
22.0	16
34.1	19.8
29.1	18.4
27.0	17.1
24.0	15.5
20.9	14.7
27.8	17.1
20.8	15.4
28.5	16.2
26.4	15
28.1	17.2
27.0	16
28.6	17
24.6	14.4

a

To draw a line of best fit, move your ruler until approximately half the points are above the line and half below.

b Calculating the gradient m using (20, 14) and (30, 18),

$$m = \frac{18 - 14}{30 - 20} = \frac{4}{10} = 0.4$$

This is using $y = mx + c$ but with N and T instead of x and y.

c is given by the N-intercept ≈ 6.5
So the equation is $N = 0.4T + 6.5$

c Substituting $T = 30$, $N = 0.4 \times 30 + 6.5$
$= 12 + 6.5$
$= 18.5$

You would expect to hear 18.5 chirps per second.

d 10°C is outside of the range that you have data for.
Therefore you do not know if the rule will still be valid.

EXAMINER'S TIP

As this question uses 'real' data the points do not lie exactly on a straight line, so you need to draw a line of best fit. In some situations the points may lie exactly on a straight line.

Exercise BA2

MEDIUM HIGH

1   For each of the following data sets:
    i   plot the points
    ii draw a line through the points (it may be either exact or a line of best fit)
    iii find an equation relating the two variables.
    Draw each graph on a separate set of axes and choose
    scales to make each graph as large as possible.

a			b			c			d			e			f	
m	r		g	n		t	R		w	s		n	Q		r	b
3	37		3	13		3	24		3	0		23	18		132	8
10	72		10	24		10	22		10	38		32	22		286	32
8	62		8	21		8	23		8	33		19	16		417	60
21	127		21	42		21	19		21	100		22	18		333	47
32	182		32	60		32	15		32	185		30	22		613	110
12	82		12	28		12	21		12	46		16	14		541	83
43	237		43	77		43	12		43	230		29	21		189	19
26	152		26	50		26	17		26	138		26	17		377	54

2   Barney is cooking roast beef for his family. He looks in a recipe
    book for cooking instructions and then looks on the Internet.

Roast Beef
15 mins per
pound
+
an extra 30 mins

Recipe

Roast beef
20 mins per pound
+
an extra 20 mins

The recipe book leads to a formula of $C = 20w + 20$ where C is the
cooking time in minutes and w is the weight of the beef in pounds.
    a   Write a formula for the cooking time based on the Internet recipe.
    b   On the same set of axes draw graphs to represent the cooking
            times for **both** sets of instructions for $0 \le w \le 6$.
    c   Use your graphs to find the weight of beef for which **both** sets of
            instructions give the **same** cooking time.
    d   Form and solve an equation in w to verify your answer from **c**.

3   Juliet thinks there is a linear relationship between the length of a plane flight
    and the cost of a ticket. She looked up the price of the cheapest one-way
    ticket on 1 September with the same national airline from London to each
    of these destinations. She found their distance from London using the Internet.

City	Paris	Berlin	Prague	Helsinki	Brussels	Warsaw	Lyon	Oslo
Distance (m)	213	578	643	1131	198	899	458	716
Cost (£)	59	73	105	74	69	79	69	68

    a   Plot these data on a grid and draw a line of best fit through the points.
    b   Work out the equation of your line.
    c   Comment on Juliet's idea.

UNIT B

Simultaneous equations

- Two or more equations that must be solved together to find the unknowns are called **simultaneous equations**. They can be solved by first **eliminating** either x or y.

> ← LOOK BACK
> See topic AA1 on page 16 and AA6 on page 24 to revise basic algebra and equations.

Here is a pair of simultaneous equations:

$$3x + 2y = 11 \quad (1)$$
$$x + 2y = 9 \quad (2)$$

The coefficients of y are the same, so **subtract** the equations to eliminate y.

$(1) - (2)$ eliminates y
giving $2x = 2$

Here is another pair of simultaneous equations:

$$4x + 3y = 9 \quad (1)$$
$$x - 3y = 6 \quad (2)$$

The coefficients of y are the same but one is negative, so **add** the equations to eliminate y.

$(1) + (2)$ eliminates y
giving $5x = 15$

EXAMPLE

Solve

a $5x + 2y = 3$
$\quad x + 2y = -1$

b $3x - 5y = 8$
$\quad 2x + 5y = 22$

a
$$5x + 2y = 3 \quad (1)$$
$$x + 2y = -1 \quad (2)$$
$(1) - (2) \qquad 4x = 4$ so $x = 1$
Substitute in (1) $\quad 5 + 2y = 3$
$\qquad\qquad 2y = -2$ so $y = -1$
Solution is $x = 1$, $y = -1$

b
$$3x - 5y = 8 \quad (1)$$
$$2x + 5y = 22 \quad (2)$$
$(1) + (2) \qquad 5x = 30$ so $x = 6$
Substitute in (2) $\quad 12 + 5y = 22$
$\qquad\qquad 5y = 10$ so $y = 2$
Solution is $x = 6$, $y = 2$

- If the coefficients of **neither** unknown are the same, multiply one or both equations to make them the same.

EXAMPLE

Solve

a $5x + 2y = 11$
$\quad 7x - 8y = 10$

b $3x + 4y = 3$
$\quad 5x + 3y = 16$

> Check your values by substituting into each equation to see if they both work.

a
$$5x + 2y = 11 \quad (1)$$
$$7x - 8y = 10 \quad (2)$$
$(1) \times 4 \qquad 20x + 8y = 44 \quad (3)$
$(3) + (2) \qquad\quad 27x = 54$ so $x = 2$
Substitute in (1) $\quad 10 + 2y = 11$
$\qquad\qquad 2y = 1$ so $y = \dfrac{1}{2}$

The solution is $x = 2$, $y = \dfrac{1}{2}$

b
$$3x + 4y = 3 \quad (1)$$
$$5x + 3y = 16 \quad (2)$$
$(1) \times 3 \qquad 9x + 12y = 9 \quad (3)$
$(2) \times 4 \qquad 20x + 12y = 64 \quad (4)$
$(4) - (3) \qquad\quad 11x = 55$ so $x = 5$
Substitute in (2) $\quad 25 + 3y = 16$
$\qquad\qquad 3y = -9$ so $y = -3$

The solution is $x = 5$, $y = -3$

You may also have to **form simultaneous equations** from real-life problems (see questions 2 and 3 in the exercise).

Exercise BA3

MEDIUM HIGH

1 Solve these pairs of simultaneous equations.

   a $3x + y = 19$
      $2x + y = 15$

   b $x + 3y = 3$
      $4x - 3y = 27$

   c $8x + y = 41$
      $8x - 2y = 14$

   d $7c - 2d = 23$
      $3c - 2d = 11$

   e $3x + 4y = 31$
      $2x + y = 14$

   f $2x + y = 12$
      $10x - 3y = 4$

   g $6x + y = 0$
      $2x - 3y = 10$

   h $3p + 11q = 19$
      $9p - 2q = 92$

   i $11x - y = 29$
      $2x - 5y = 39$

   j $3x + 5y = 14$
      $5x - 2y = 44$

   k $3x + 7y = 55$
      $4x + 5y = 43$

   l $5x - 2y = 94$
      $3x - 7y = 39$

   m $15l + 8m = 1$
      $9l - 10m = 8$

   n $5x - 3y = 23$
      $2y = x - 14$

   o $0.6g + 0.7h = 2.5$
      $0.5g - 1.1h = 10.5$

> **EXAMINER'S TIP:**
> - Simultaneous equations may have negative or fractional solutions.
> - Don't make the common mistake of only giving the answer to one of your unknowns!

2 Jo buys 3 coffees and 2 muffins for £9.60.
Lizzie buys 7 muffins and 2 coffees for £14.90.
Form and solve simultaneous equations to find the cost of 1 coffee and 1 muffin.

3 A farmer keeps chickens and pigs.
He can sell a chicken for £2 and a pig for £50.
He has c chickens and p pigs.

   a **i** How many legs do p pigs have?

      ii How many heads do c chickens have?

One day the farmer counts the legs of all his pigs and chickens and gets 208.

   b Write an equation in p and c.

The farmer then counts the heads of his pigs and chickens and gets 83.

   c Write a second equation in p and c. Solve your two equations and hence find how much money the farmer will raise if he sells all his pigs and chickens.

4 Try to solve these simultaneous equations.

$$2x - 7y = 20$$
$$6x - 21y = 60$$

Explain what your solution tells you about the graphs of

$$2x - 7y = 20$$
$$\text{and } 6x - 21y = 60$$

Inequalities

- An **inequality** is a mathematical statement involving one or more inequality **symbols**.
  The inequality symbols are $<$, $\leq$, $>$ and $\geq$

Inequalities can be represented on a **number line**.
Inequalities are solved using **inverse operations** in the same way as linear equations.
However if you **multiply** or **divide** each side by a **negative number** you **reverse** the inequality. $6 > 4$ but $-6 < -4$

EXAMPLE

Solve these inequalities.
Represent the answer to part **c** on a number line.

> If you started by adding $2x$ to each side, you could avoid dividing by a negative.

a $3x - 7 \leq 23$ **b** $4 - 2x > 10$ **c** $11 \leq 5m + 6 < 26$

- -

a $3x - 7 \leq 23$
    $3x \leq 30$ Add 7 to each side
     $x \leq 10$ Divide each side by 3

b $4 - 2x > 10$
    $-2x > 6$ Subtract 4 from each side
    $x < -3$ Divide by -2 so reverse inequality

c $11 \leq 5m + 6 < 26$
    $5 \leq 5m < 20$ Subtract 6 from each term
    $1 \leq m < 4$ Divide each term by 5

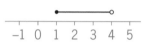

- An inequality in **two variables** can be represented by a **region** on a graph.

EXAMPLE

Represent using shading the region satisfied by all of these inequalities:

$x \geq 1$, $y \leq 5$ and $y \geq 2x - 2$.

- -

Start by drawing the lines $x = 1$, $y = 5$ and $y = 2x - 2$.

Then shade the region you **don't** want.

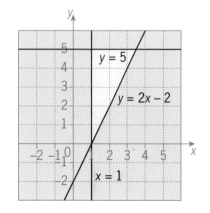

EXAMINER'S TIP

Examiners don't mind if you shade **in** the region required or shade it **out**.

However make sure the region is clear – you may want to write an **R** in it.

> For $y \geq 2x - 2$, choose any point **not** on the line, say $(4, 3)$.
> Here $y = 3$ and $2x - 2 = 6$.
> 3 is not ≥ 6 so the inequality **doesn't** hold.
> So that side of the line is shaded **out**.

> If the inequalities are $<$ or $>$ the lines should be drawn broken or dashed.

Exercise BA4

MEDIUM HIGH

1 Solve these inequalities.

   a $x + 3 > 9$
   b $8x > 40$
   c $x - 9 < 16$

   d $\dfrac{y}{6} \le 10$
   e $2x + 3 \ge 10$
   f $4p - 7 \le 11$

   g $\dfrac{d}{3} - 4 > 2$
   h $\dfrac{f}{5} + 6 < 9$
   i $3(r - 2) > 1$

   j $2(3x + 5) \ge 2 - 2x$
   k $3 - 5x > -2$
   l $-3x \le 30$

   m $2 - v \le 5 - 7v$
   n $5c + 6 > 3c + 2(6 - c)$
   o $\dfrac{r}{3} > \dfrac{r+2}{2}$

   p $-1 < 2x < 10$
   q $3 < x + 5 < 12$
   r $5 \le 2x - 9 \le 14$

2 Represent your answers to question 1 parts **a, e, i, m** and **q** on number lines.

3 Dave has 3 packets of mints and 7 loose mints.
Ann has 1 packet of mints and 25 loose mints.
Dave has **at least** as many mints as Ann.
Let m be the number of mints in a packet.
Form and solve an inequality in m.
What is the **smallest** number of mints that could be in each packet?

4 Use inequalities to describe the **unshaded** regions.

   a

   b
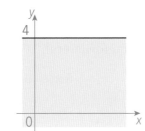

   c
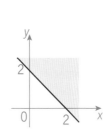

   d
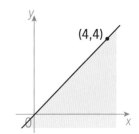

5 Draw sketch graphs to represent these inequalities. Leave the required region **unshaded**.

   a $x \le 5$
   b $y \ge -3$
   c $x \le y$
   d $x + y \le 6$

   e $y < 2x - 4$
   f $y > \frac{1}{2}x + 7$
   g $x + 2y < 8$
   h $3x - 4y \ge 12$

6 Represent using shading the region satisfied by all of these inequalities.
Leave the required region **unshaded**.
Use a separate set of axes for each part of this question.

   a $x \ge 3,\quad y \ge 0,\quad x + y \le 5$
   b $x \ge 1,\quad y \ge x,\quad 2x + y \le 10$

7 Murphy's the baker sells white rolls at 10p each and granary rolls at 12p each.
Mrs Honeyman buys at least 6 white rolls; she also buys more than twice as
many granary rolls as white; and she buys fewer than 20 rolls in total.

   a If she buys w white rolls and g granary rolls, explain why $g > 2w$
       and write down two further inequalities in g and w.

   b Represent your inequalities on a graph, and explain why your graph shows
       there is only one possible value for the number of each type of roll she bought.

   c How much does Mrs Honeyman spend on her rolls?

Angles, triangles and quadrilaterals

Learn these angle facts.

Angles and straight lines

Angles at a point add up to 360°.

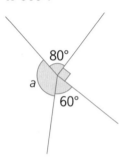

$a + 80° + 90° + 60° = 360°$
$a = 360° − 230° = 130°$

Opposite angles are equal.

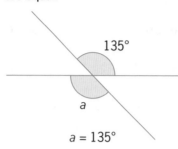

$a = 135°$

Angles that make up a half turn add up to 180°.

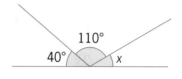

$x + 40° + 110° = 180°$
$x = 180° − 150° = 30°$

You should learn the rules for angles and parallel lines.

Alternate angles are equal.

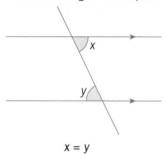

$x = y$

Corresponding angles are equal.

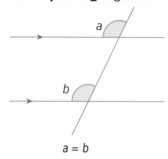

$a = b$

Interior angles sum to 180°.

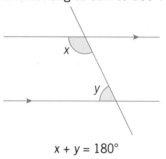

$x + y = 180°$

Remember these facts about angles in a triangle or a quadrilateral.

Triangle

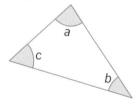

$a + b + c = 180°$

Quadrilateral

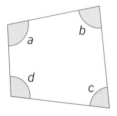

$a + b + c + d = 360°$

Remember these triangles:

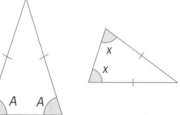

Isosceles

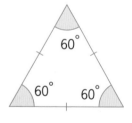

Equilateral

Find the unknown angles shown by letters in these diagrams (which are not drawn to scale).

a

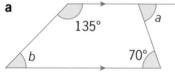

b

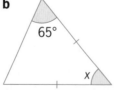

c

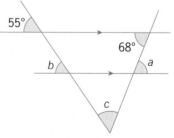

a $a = 70°$ (alternate)
$b = 180° − 135° = 45°$
(interior angles)

b $x = 180° − 2 × 65° = 50°$

c $a = 68°$ (alternate)
$b = 55°$ (corresponding)
$c = 180° − (68° + 55°) = 57°$
(triangle sum)

Find the unknown angles, giving reasons for your answers.

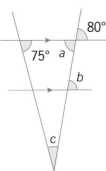

$a = 85°$ (alternate)
$b = 70°$ (alternate)
$c = 180° - (70° + 85°) = 25°$
(triangle sum)
$d = 25°$ (opposite angles equal)

Exercise BG1

MEDIUM

1 Find the unknown angles indicated by letters in these diagrams.

a

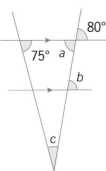

b

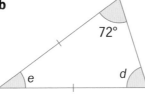

c

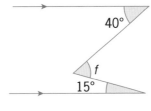

d

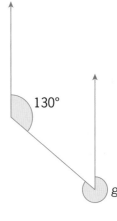

e

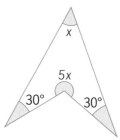

f

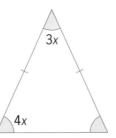

2 Find the unknown angles, giving reasons and leaving your answers in fractional form as appropriate.

a

b

3 Using this diagram and the properties of parallel lines explain carefully why the sum of the three angles in any triangle must be 180°.

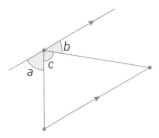

4 **a** Use this diagram to prove an important relationship between the angles a, b and c.

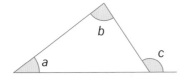

b Using this result or otherwise find the value of x in this diagram.

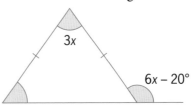

UNIT B

A **quadrilateral** is a polygon with four sides. There are several different types of quadrilateral and they each have their own properties.

square	rhombus	rectangle	parallelogram	trapezium	kite
A	**B**	**C**	**D**	**E**	**F**

   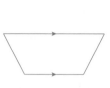

A five-sided polygon is called a **pentagon** and a six-sided polygon is a **hexagon.**

You can divide a pentagon into 3 triangles so the sum of its 5 interior angles must be 3 × 180° = 540°

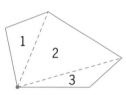

You can divide a hexagon into 4 triangles so the sum of its 6 interior angles = 4 × 180° = 720°

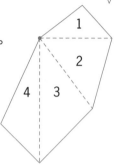

These diagrams show the **exterior angles** of

a quadrilateral

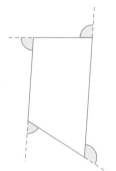

a pentagon

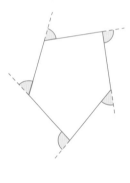

The sum of the exterior angles of any polygon is always 360°.

Polygons with all sides equal and all angles equal are called **regular polygons**.

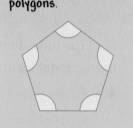

EXAMPLE

a Find the unknown angles in the pentagon below.

b Find the size of one exterior angle of a regular pentagon. Hence find the interior angle.

a The sum of the interior angles of a pentagon = 3 × 180° = 540°

$5x + 335° = 540°$
$5x \quad\quad = 205°$
$x \quad\quad = 205° ÷ 5$
$\quad\quad = 41°$

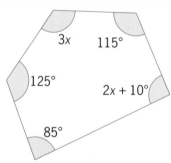

Therefore the unknown angles are 3 × 41° = 123° and 2 × 41° + 10° = 92°

b Exterior angle = $\frac{360°}{5}$ = 72°

Interior angle = 180° − 72° = 108°

Exercise BG2

1 Find the unknown angles in these diagrams.

a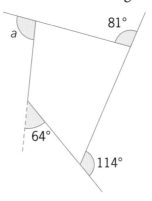

b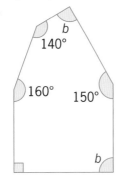

c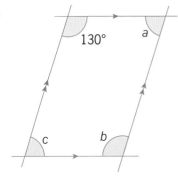

2 a By dividing the octagon into triangles find the total interior angle sum for an octagon.

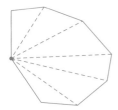

b Use this fact to calculate the size of x in this diagram.

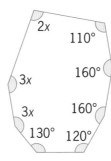

3 a David wants to draw a regular pentagon. He starts by drawing a circle radius 4 cm.
   Write down clear instructions so that he can draw a regular pentagon using this circle.

b How could he draw a regular hexagon?

c Write instructions that work for any polygon.

4 A garden is designed in the shape of a regular enneagon (9-sided polygon).
   Calculate the size of one interior angle of this polygon and hence the size of one exterior angle.

> This is also called a nonagon.

5 a Find the total interior angle sum for a regular 20-sided polygon. Hence find the size of one interior angle.

b Show that this is correct by calculating the size of one exterior angle of the polygon and using this to find the size of an interior angle.
   In both cases explain carefully what your method is.

6 Could regular pentagons be used to tile a floor leaving no spaces? What about regular hexagons? Explain your answers clearly.

> Tiling without leaving spaces is called tessellation.

7 A regular polygon has n sides. Using the exterior angle sum property for a polygon, formulate a general rule for calculating the size of one interior angle x. Test your formula by finding the interior angle of a regular hexagon.

Circle theorems

You can use these **circle theorems** to find unknown angles.

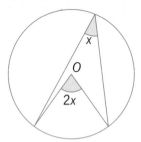

Angle at centre is twice angle at circumference.

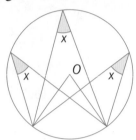

Angle in a semicircle is a right angle.

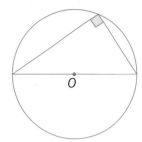

Angles in same segment are equal.

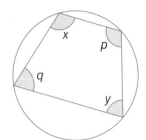

Opposite angles in a cyclic quadrilateral sum to 180°, for example, $p + q = 180°$.

Note that the first theorem implies the second. If the angle at the centre is increased to 180° then the angle at the circumference becomes a right angle and this is the second theorem.

EXAMPLE

Find the unknown value x.

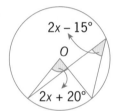

$2x + 20° = 2(2x − 15°)$ (angle at centre twice angle at circumference)

$2x + 20° = 4x − 30°$ (expand brackets)

$50° = 2x$

$x = 25°$

- A line that touches a circle at exactly one point is called a **tangent** to the circle.

There are three theorems about tangents to circles.

A tangent forms a right angle with a radius.

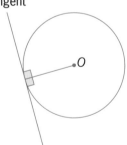

Tangents from a point outside circle are equal in length.

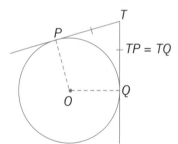

$TP = TQ$

Angle between tangent and chord is equal to angle in alternate segment.

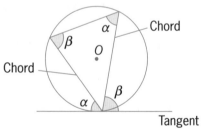

EXAMPLE

Find the angle OBA.
Explain your method carefully.

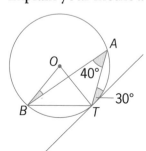

angle $TOB = 80°$ (angle at centre twice angle at circumference)

angle $OBT = \dfrac{180° − 80°}{2} = 50°$ ($\triangle OBT$ isosceles)

angle $ABT = 30°$ (alternate segment theorem)

∴ angle $OBA = 50° − 30° = 20°$

1 Find the unknown angles indicated by letters in these diagrams.
Give reasons for your answers.

a

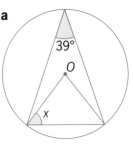

b

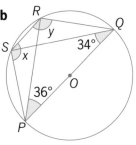

c

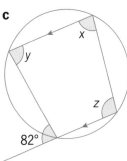

d

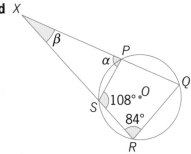

e

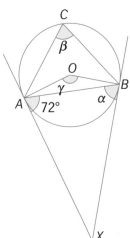

f

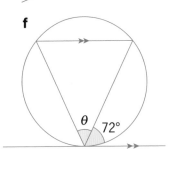

2 Find in terms of x the angles AOB, BAE and BDA. What conclusion can you draw from these results?

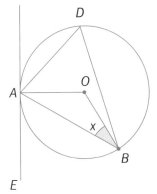

3 Find in terms of y the angles OQP and OPQ, where O is the centre of the circle.
Hence explain why AB is parallel to PQ.

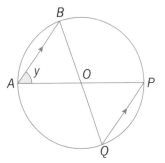

4 Is the quadrilateral $PQRS$ a rectangle? Explain your answer carefully.

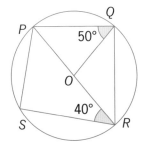

5 If $OP = PQ$ prove that $RQ = PQ$.

UNIT B

Symmetry, reflection and rotation

An equilateral triangle has a high degree of symmetry. It has three lines of **reflection** symmetry (sometimes called line symmetry) and **rotation** symmetry order 3.

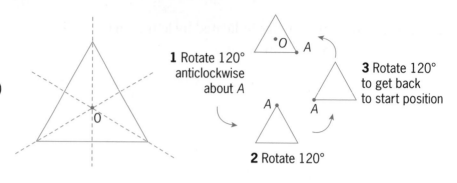

1 Rotate 120° anticlockwise about A

2 Rotate 120°

3 Rotate 120° to get back to start position

---

* A line of symmetry divides a shape into identical halves.

A parallelogram has no lines of reflection symmetry. You can **justify** this by looking at point X.

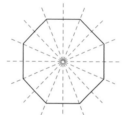

EXAMPLE

Write down the number of lines of symmetry and the order of rotation symmetry of these shapes.

rectangle

2 lines of symmetry
rotation symmetry order 2

octagon

16 lines of symmetry
rotation symmetry order 8

The image of X is not on the parallelogram. Now look at the other diagonal.

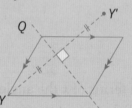

The image of Y is not on the parallelogram either.

---

* You describe a rotation by naming the **centre**, direction and **angle** of rotation.
* You describe a reflection by naming the mirror line.

Every shape has rotation symmetry of at least order 1 (a complete turn brings the shape back to its original position).

Points on the mirror line don't move.

EXAMPLE

a Reflect the triangle X in the line $x = 3$.
b Rotate the triangle X through 90° about the centre (2, 0).
c Reflect the triangle X in the line $y = 0$.

The line y = 0 is the x-axis.

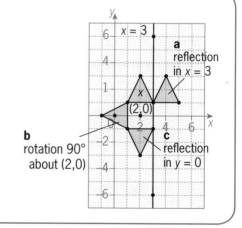

a reflection in x = 3

b rotation 90° about (2,0)

c reflection in y = 0

Exercise BG4

MEDIUM

1 Copy the diagram and use the lines of symmetry
to draw the complete shapes.
What is the order of rotation symmetry of each shape?

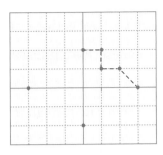

2 Copy the diagram onto a set of axes from −10 to 10.
Reflect triangle K in

  a the x-axis

  b the line $y = 1$

  c the line $y = x$.

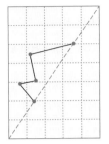

3 On axes labelled from −6 to +6 plot A (1, 1), B (4, 2),
C (3, 4) and join the points to make triangle ABC.

  a Rotate triangle ABC through 90° about (−1, 0) and label
the image triangle T.

  b Reflect T in the y-axis and label the image U.

4 Describe fully the transformation of trapezium A onto

  a T_1 **b** T_2

5 What single reflection is equivalent to a reflection in the
line $x = 1$ followed by a reflection in the line $x = 3$ followed
by a reflection in the line $x = 6$?

6 Draw x and y-axes from −6 to 6. Draw the line $y = x$.
Plot the triangle with vertices at (3, 1), (4, 2) and (6, 1)
and label it P.

  a Reflect P in the x-axis and label the image Q.

  b Reflect Q in the line $y = x$ and label this image R.

  c Describe fully the transformation that maps triangle P
directly onto triangle R.

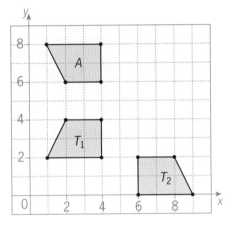

7 Draw x and y-axes from −6 to 6. Plot triangle S with
vertices (2, 1), (5, 1) and (5, 3).

  a Rotate S through 90° about the origin. Label the
image T.

  b Reflect T in the y-axis and label the image U.

  c Describe fully the single transformation which maps S
onto U.

UNIT B

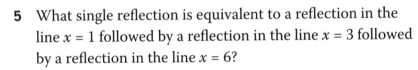

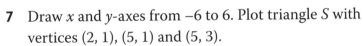

When you **translate** an **object** you change its position without
rotating, reflecting or enlarging it.

You describe a translation with a **column vector** $\begin{pmatrix} x \\ y \end{pmatrix}$.

> x is the distance moved left or right,
> y is the distance moved up or down.

EXAMPLE

Translate triangle T using the vectors

a $\begin{pmatrix} 3 \\ 2 \end{pmatrix}$ **b** $\begin{pmatrix} -2 \\ -4 \end{pmatrix}$ **c** $\begin{pmatrix} 5 \\ 0 \end{pmatrix}$

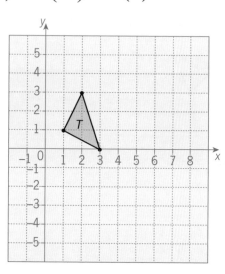

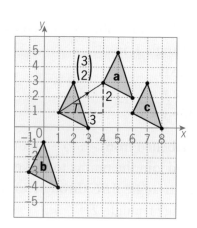

Shapes can be changed and moved through a sequence of transformations.

EXAMPLE

The triangle P has vertices $(2, 1)$, $(4, 1)$ and $(4, 2)$.

a   Reflect P in the y-axis. Label the image triangle Q.
Reflect Q in the x-axis and label the image R.
What single transformation would map R back onto the original triangle P?

b   Reflect P in the line $x = 2$. Label the image A.
Reflect triangle A in the line $x = 3$ to form the image B.
What single transformation would map P directly onto B?

- -

a   Either by observation or using tracing paper you can
see that a rotation of $180°$ about the origin would map R
back onto P.

b   The single transformation equivalent to these two
reflections would be a translation with vector $\begin{pmatrix} 2 \\ 0 \end{pmatrix}$.

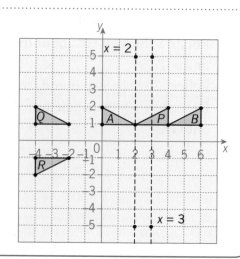

Describe fully the single transformation which is equivalent to
a a reflection in the line $y = x$ followed by a reflection in the y-axis
b a rotation of 90°, centre the origin, followed by a reflection in the line $y = -x$.

a

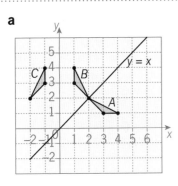

Start with triangle A.
Reflect in $y = x$ to give triangle B.
Reflect B in the y-axis to give C.
By observation or using tracing paper the transformation from A to C is a rotation of 90°, centre the origin.

b

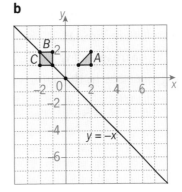

Start with triangle A.
Rotate to B.
Reflect to C.
Overall this is a reflection in the y-axis.

Exercise BG5

MEDIUM

1 Describe the transformation that maps $\triangle ABC$ onto $\triangle A'B'C'$.
What transformation maps $\triangle A'B'C'$ back to $\triangle ABC$?

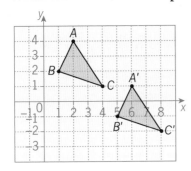

2 a What single transformation is equivalent to a reflection in the line $x = 1$ followed by a reflection in the line $x = 4$?

b What single transformation is equivalent to a reflection in the line $y = 2$ followed by a reflection in the line $y = -1$?

3 P is a triangle with vertices (3, 3), (1, 2) and (4, 1).

a P is reflected in the x-axis and then translated using the vector $\begin{pmatrix} -5 \\ 0 \end{pmatrix}$. Find the coordinates of the vertices of the final image of P.

b P is rotated 90° about the point (2, 1) and then reflected in the line $x = -1$. Write down the coordinates of the vertices of the final image of P.

4 $\triangle XYZ$ has vertices (−4, 1), (−6, 4) and (−3, 2).

a Rotate $\triangle XYZ$ anticlockwise 90° about (−1, 2) and label the new triangle $X'Y'Z'$.

b Reflect $\triangle X'Y'Z'$ in the line $x = -1$ and label this triangle $X''Y''Z''$.

c What single transformation would map $\triangle XYZ$ onto $\triangle X''Y''Z''$?

- **Congruent** shapes are identical. One shape can be placed exactly on top of the other.
- **Similar** shapes have the same shape but are different sizes. For example, all circles are similar.
- In similar shapes the **corresponding** angles are equal and the corresponding sides are in the same ratio.

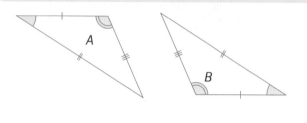

Triangles *A* and *B* are congruent.

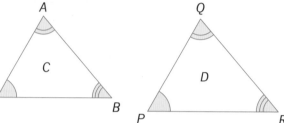

Triangles *C* and *D* are similar.

EXAMPLE

Refer to the diagram.

a Prove that $\triangle OAB$ and $\triangle OCD$ are similar.

b Find the length of *CD*.

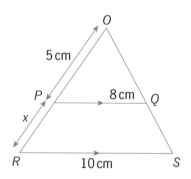

a angle *AOB* = angle *COD* (opposite angles equal)
angle *BAO* = angle *CDO* (alternate angles equal)
angle *ABO* = angle *OCD* (alternate angles equal)
The corresponding angles are equal therefore $\triangle OAB$ and $\triangle OCD$ are similar.

b *CD* corresponds to *AB* and *OA* corresponds to *OD*.

$$\frac{CD}{AB} = \frac{DO}{AO} \text{ hence } \frac{CD}{5} = \frac{12}{3} = 4 \text{ so } CD = 5 \times 4 = 20\,\text{cm}$$

EXAMPLE

Using the diagram

a prove that $\triangle OPQ$ and $\triangle ORS$ are similar

b hence determine the length *x*.

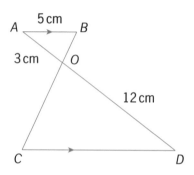

a angle *ROS* is common to both triangles.
angle *OPQ* = angle *ORS* (corresponding angles)
angle *OQP* = angle *OSR* (corresponding angles)
The corresponding angles are equal so the triangles are similar.

b *OP* corresponds to *OR* and *PQ* corresponds to *RS*.

$$\frac{RS}{PQ} = \frac{OR}{OP} \quad \text{so} \quad \frac{10}{8} = \frac{5+x}{5} \text{ or } 1.25 = \frac{5+x}{5}$$

so $5 \times 1.25 = 5 + x$, hence $x = 6.25 - 5 = 1.25\,\text{cm}$

Exercise BG6

MEDIUM HIGH

1 The three triangles in the diagram are similar. Find the lengths *a* and *b* (all lengths are cm).

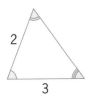
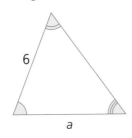
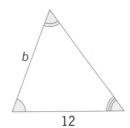

2 a Prove △*PQR* is similar to △*PTS*.
  b Find the missing length *x*.

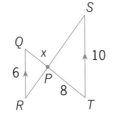

> Take care to identify which angles and sides correspond. Show clear stages of working,

3 A vertical stick of length 1.4 m casts a shadow of 2.2 m.
A nearby tree casts a shadow of 14 m.
Find the height of the tree.

4 A cone is cut parallel to its base to form a smaller cone.
Find the radius *r* of the smaller cone.

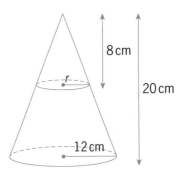

5 A light is shone on to a screen, through a hole in a piece of cardboard. The diameter of the hole AB is 4 cm. The spot of light on the screen, CO, has diameter 10 cm. If the cardboard is 5 cm from the light show that the screen is 12.5 cm from the light.

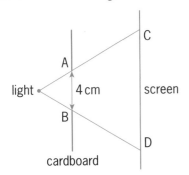

> With problems like this a diagram helps, so if one is not given draw your own.

6 Find the length *x* in this diagram. Show your method clearly.

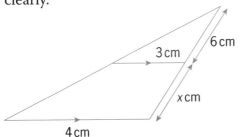

- **Congruent** shapes are identical.
- If two shapes are **similar** one is an **enlargement** of the other.

You describe an enlargement by naming the **centre** and the **scale factor**.
Scale factors can be fractional and negative.

Enlarge triangle P with centre O and scale factor

a 2 **b** −2

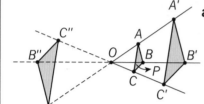

a $OA' = 2OA$ **b** $OA'' = 2OA$
$OB' = 2OB$ $OB'' = 2OB$
$OC' = 2OC$ $OC'' = 2OC$

Plot the points $A(3, 2)$, $B(6, 2)$, $C(5, 4)$ and $D(4, 4)$ and
join them up to form a trapezium.

a Using the centre O (4.5, 3) and scale factor 2 enlarge
the trapezium.

b Using centre O (3, 5) and scale factor $\frac{1}{2}$ enlarge the
trapezium.

a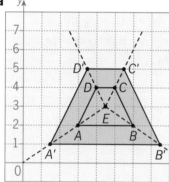

b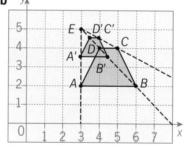

$EA' = 2OA$ $EA' = 0.5OA$
$EB' = 2EB$ and so on. $EB' = 0.5OB$ and so on.

Notice that when the scale factor is a fraction between 0 and 1,
the image is smaller than the object, that is, the enlargement is
reduced in size – but it is still called an enlargement.

The scale factor −1 is equivalent to
a rotation of 180°.

Sometimes you have to find the centre and the scale factor of an
enlargement from the object and its image.

Find the centre and scale factor of enlargement of trapezium P shown in the diagram.

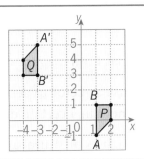

Join A to A' and B to B'. AA' and BB' intersect at the centre of enlargement $O\,(-1, 2)$.

$OA' = -OA$

The scale factor of the enlargement $= \dfrac{OA}{OA'} = \dfrac{OA}{-OA} = -1$

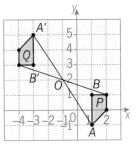

Exercise BG7

MEDIUM HIGH

1   On a blank piece of paper copy this diagram and the centre of enlargement O.
    Enlarge the shape by scale factor 3.

Do a rough sketch first to make sure you have enough space.

2   Copy the diagram and shape onto a grid with axes from 8 to −8, and enlarge the given shape P as instructed.
    a Scale factor 2, centre $(0, 0)$
    b Scale factor 0.5, centre $(6, 6)$
    c Scale factor −1, centre the origin.

3   Triangle ABC with $A(1, 9)$, $B(5, 1)$, $C(1, 1)$ is enlarged to triangle PQR with $P(2, 8)$, $Q(5, 2)$ and $R(2, 2)$.
    a Draw the triangles ABC and PQR.
    b Write down the centre of the enlargement.
    c State the scale factor of the enlargement.

4   The points $A(5, 3)$, $B(9, 7)$, $C(13, -1)$ and $D(7, -1)$ form a quadrilateral.
    a Plot the points A, B, C and D and draw the quadrilateral.
    b Using $(5, 1)$ as the centre of enlargement, enlarge $ABCD$ by scale factor $\dfrac{1}{2}$.
    c Write down the coordinates of the vertices of the image.

5   The triangle A is enlarged, centre O, to give the larger triangle B. Find the unknown length x.

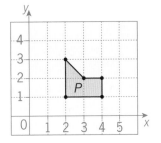

6   Fraser has a photograph 15 cm × 10 cm. Could this photograph be mathematically enlarged to the following dimensions?
    Provide clear reasoning for your answers.
    a 30 cm × 20 cm   **b** 18.75 cm × 12.5 cm   **c** 7.5 cm × 6 cm
    d 3 cm × 2 cm   **e** 67.5 cm × 45 cm   **f** 52.5 cm × 33.5 cm

Vectors and vector geometry

A **vector** has both magnitude (size) and direction.

You can use a vector to describe a translation, which is a displacement in a certain direction.

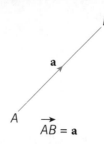

Forces (such as pressure) and velocity (speed in a certain direction) can also be described using vectors.

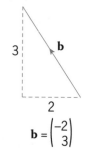

The diagram shows how to represent a vector.

$\overrightarrow{AB} = \mathbf{a}$

$\mathbf{b} = \begin{pmatrix} -2 \\ 3 \end{pmatrix}$

Vectors can be added, subtracted and multiplied by numbers.

a denotes just the length of the vector.
b denotes the length and the direction.

EXAMPLE

If $\mathbf{p} = \begin{pmatrix} 2 \\ 3 \end{pmatrix}$, $\mathbf{q} = \begin{pmatrix} 4 \\ -1 \end{pmatrix}$, $\mathbf{r} = \begin{pmatrix} -2 \\ 5 \end{pmatrix}$ find **a** $\mathbf{p} + \mathbf{q}$ **b** $3\mathbf{p}$ **c** $-\mathbf{r}$

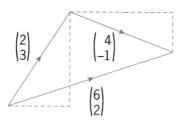

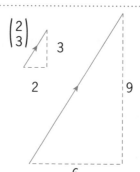

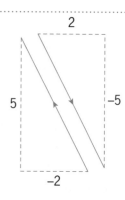

a $\mathbf{p} + \mathbf{q} = \begin{pmatrix} 2 \\ 3 \end{pmatrix} + \begin{pmatrix} 4 \\ -1 \end{pmatrix} = \begin{pmatrix} 2+4 \\ 3-1 \end{pmatrix} = \begin{pmatrix} 6 \\ 2 \end{pmatrix}$ **b** $3\mathbf{p} = 3\begin{pmatrix} 2 \\ 3 \end{pmatrix} = \begin{pmatrix} 6 \\ 9 \end{pmatrix}$ **c** $-\mathbf{r} = -\begin{pmatrix} -2 \\ 5 \end{pmatrix} = \begin{pmatrix} 2 \\ -5 \end{pmatrix}$

$\begin{pmatrix} 6 \\ 2 \end{pmatrix}$ is the **resultant** vector.

Multiplying by a number stretches the original vector.

Changing sign changes the direction of the vector.

You do not always know the numerical components of a vector.

EXAMPLE

In the diagram $\overrightarrow{OA} = \mathbf{a}$ and $\overrightarrow{OB} = \mathbf{b}$.

a Find $\overrightarrow{AB}$ and $\overrightarrow{BA}$ in terms of **a** and **b**.

b If M is the midpoint of AB find the vector $\overrightarrow{OM}$ in terms of **a** and **b**.

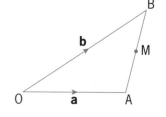

a $\overrightarrow{AB} = -\overrightarrow{OA} + \overrightarrow{OB} = -\mathbf{a} + \mathbf{b} = \mathbf{b} - \mathbf{a}$
$\overrightarrow{BA} = -\overrightarrow{BO} + \overrightarrow{OA} = -\mathbf{b} + \mathbf{a} = \mathbf{a} - \mathbf{b}$

b $\overrightarrow{OM} = \overrightarrow{OA} + \frac{1}{2}\overrightarrow{AB} = \overrightarrow{OA} + \frac{1}{2}(\overrightarrow{AO} + \overrightarrow{OB}) = \mathbf{a} + \frac{1}{2}(-\mathbf{a} + \mathbf{b})$

$= \mathbf{a} - \frac{\mathbf{a}}{2} + \frac{\mathbf{b}}{2} = \frac{\mathbf{a}}{2} + \frac{\mathbf{b}}{2} = \frac{1}{2}(\mathbf{a} + \mathbf{b})$

In the diagram $\overrightarrow{OP} = \mathbf{p}$ and $\overrightarrow{OR} = \mathbf{r}$. T divides QP in the ratio $5 : 1$.

M is the midpoint of RQ.

Find in terms of $\mathbf{p}$ and $\mathbf{r}$ the vectors $\overrightarrow{OT}$, $\overrightarrow{OM}$ and $\overrightarrow{MT}$.

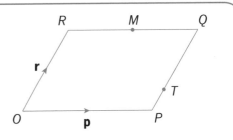

$$\overrightarrow{OT} = \overrightarrow{OP} + \frac{1}{6}\overrightarrow{PQ} = \mathbf{p} + \frac{1}{6}\mathbf{r}$$

$$\overrightarrow{OM} = \overrightarrow{OR} + \frac{1}{2}\overrightarrow{RQ} = \mathbf{r} + \frac{1}{2}\mathbf{p}$$

$$\overrightarrow{MT} = \overrightarrow{MQ} + \overrightarrow{QT} = \frac{1}{2}\mathbf{p} - \frac{5}{6}\mathbf{r}$$

Exercise BG8

HIGH

1   In the regular hexagon $ABCDEF$, $\overrightarrow{AF} = \mathbf{r}$, $\overrightarrow{AB} = \mathbf{q}$ and $\overrightarrow{BC} = \mathbf{p}$.

Find in terms of $\mathbf{r}$, $\mathbf{q}$ and $\mathbf{p}$

   a $\overrightarrow{CD}$ **b** $\overrightarrow{BE}$ **c** $\overrightarrow{DA}$ **d** $\overrightarrow{BF}$ **e** $\overrightarrow{BD}$

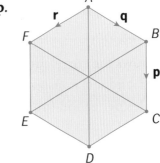

2   $\overrightarrow{OA} = \mathbf{a}$ and $\overrightarrow{OB} = \mathbf{b}$. M is the midpoint of AB.

T is the midpoint of OB. S is the midpoint of OA.

Find in terms of $\mathbf{a}$ and $\mathbf{b}$ the vectors

   a $\overrightarrow{AB}$ **b** $\overrightarrow{OM}$ **c** $\overrightarrow{MT}$ **d** $\overrightarrow{TS}$ **e** $\overrightarrow{SM}$

Give your answers in their simplest form and show your reasoning.

What conclusion can you draw from your answers to parts **c**, **d** and **e**?

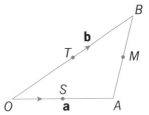

3   $OABC$ is a parallelogram.

$\overrightarrow{OC} = \mathbf{c}$ and $\overrightarrow{OA} = \mathbf{a}$.

M is the midpoint of $\overrightarrow{BC}$.

T divides AB in the ratio $4 : 1$.

Find in terms of $\mathbf{a}$ and $\mathbf{c}$

   a $\overrightarrow{OB}$ **b** $\overrightarrow{CA}$ **c** $\overrightarrow{OM}$ **d** $\overrightarrow{OT}$ **e** $\overrightarrow{MT}$

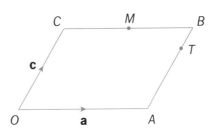

4   $OPQR$ is a parallelogram. $\overrightarrow{OP} = 3\mathbf{p} - 2\mathbf{q}$ and $\overrightarrow{OR} = 5\mathbf{p} + 6\mathbf{q}$.

   a Find $\overrightarrow{PR}$ in terms of $\mathbf{p}$ and $\mathbf{q}$.

   b T is the point where $\overrightarrow{QT} = -2\mathbf{p} + 6\mathbf{q}$.

   Does T lie on the line through P and R? Explain your answer carefully.

Scatter graphs

- A **scatter graph** shows how two sets of numerical data are related.
- **Correlation** is a measure of how the data are related.

When there is good correlation between matched pairs of data you can draw a **line of best fit**.

> **A line of best fit** is a straight line with points evenly distributed either side and does not have to pass through the origin.

Positive correlation
usually forms a line
with positive gradient

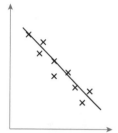

Negative correlation
usually forms a line
with negative gradient

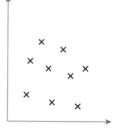

Zero correlation occurs
when it is not possible
to draw a line of best fit.

EXAMPLE

The diagram shows the correlation between engine capacity, in cm^3, and fuel consumption on motorway journeys, in miles per gallon (mpg) for 8 cars.

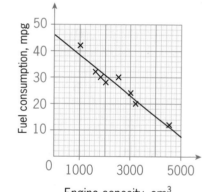

a Explain why it is appropriate to draw a line of best fit.
b Describe the correlation.
c Use the line of best fit to estimate
   i fuel consumption for 4000 cm^3 engine capacity
   ii engine capacity for a car with fuel consumption 35 mpg

....

a The points look like they lie on a straight line.
b Strong negative correlation; as engine capacity increases, fuel consumption decreases.
c i 15 mpg
   ii 1400 cm^3

Exercise BS1

MEDIUM

1   Look at the scatter diagrams below and fully describe any correlation shown.
    You may want to use words such as:
    Strong   Weak   Moderate   No correlation   Positive   Negative

         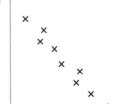

2   The table shows the scores of a multiplication test and a division
    test taken by a group of ten students.

Multiplication	25	18	15	20	16	12	14	20	18	9
Division	22	19	17	21	14	14	15	19	16	12

    a   Draw a scatter graph to display these data.
    b   Describe any correlation shown by your graph.
    c   Draw a line of best fit.
    d   Another student had taken the multiplication test and scored 23.
        Use your graph to predict her score on the division test.
    e   Explain why it may be difficult to use this graph to predict the score in
        the division test for a student who scored 6 on the multiplication test.

3   The transition times, T1 and T2 in seconds for 12 of the first 13 competitors to
    finish the 2009 London triathlon male sprint distance are recorded in the table.

T1	163	153	160	171	214	164	260	176	198	144	169	198
T2	113	114	108	106	148	132	106	106	161	109	111	138

    a   Draw a scatter diagram for these data.
    b   T1 is the time taken to change sport from swim to bike
        and T2 the time taken to change sport from bike to run.
        Comment on the T1 and T2 times shown by your scatter diagram.
    c   Part of the data for one of the first 13 males to finish this triathlon is missing.
        His T1 time was 209 seconds. If it is possible, use your graph to estimate
        his T2 time; if it is not possible explain why it is not possible.

4   The table shows the weights, to the nearest kg, and the bleep test scores for a sample of students.

Weight (kg)	45	60	57	62	48	54	49	44
Bleep test score	7.8	6.0	6.3	5.8	7.1	6.5	7.3	7.5

    a   Draw a scatter diagram to show these data.
    b   Describe any correlation shown by your graph.
    c   Draw a line of best fit on your graph.
    d   Use your line to estimate   i   the weight of a student with a bleep test score of 6.8
                                    ii   The bleep test score of a student who weighs 51 kg.

UNIT B

A time series graph displays several values of a measurement taken at different times.

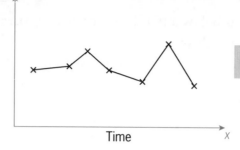

Time

Time is always on the horizontal axis.

- The **trend** of a time series graph shows the general direction over a period of time.
- **Seasonal variations** in trend are seen where the patterns of plotted points match to seasons of the year, for example heating costs (more in winter than summer).
- **Cyclical variations** are variations where the general shape of the graph has a tendency to repeat.
- **Random variations** are unpredictable and can appear in any time series graph.

EXAMPLE

The graph shows the percentage of trains operated by one company that arrived late during 2009.

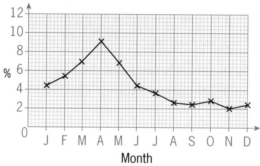

a Describe the trend shown by the graph.

b These are the percentages of late trains for the first eight months of the following year.

Month	Jan	Feb	March	April	May	June	July	Aug
% late	2.2	3	2.8	3.4	2.5	2.1	1.8	2

Describe any further trends in the data.

c Comment, with reasons, on whether the train company improved its punctuality.

a Increase in number of late trains in first few months, but towards the end of the year only approximately 2% of trains were late.

b It appears that the trend follows the same pattern as the previous year with an increase to a peak in April and then decrease.

c The trend appears to be the same in both years. In the second year, the peak in April is lower, also the months leading up to that have a

Give mathematical reasons.
As well as a reason give a final conclusion to answer the question.

Exercise BS2

1 The numbers of ASBOs, to the nearest 100, issued each year from 2002 to 2008 are given in the table.

An ASBO is an Anti-Social Behaviour Order, issued by courts in the UK for minor offences.

Year	2002	2003	2004	2005	2006	2007	2008
ASBOs	400	1300	3500	4100	2700	2300	2000

  a Draw a time series graph to represent these data.

  b Comment on any trend shown by your graph.

2 The graph shows the temperature, taken at 4 hourly intervals, of a hospital patient suffering from a virus.

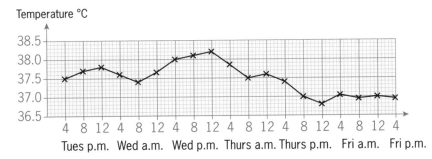

Normal temperature is 36.9 °C.

  a When was the patient most ill?

  b When would you say the patient is well enough to get up? Give mathematical reasons for your answer.

3 The table gives the termly sales turnover, to the nearest £100, for a school canteen.

	2004	2005	2006	2007
Spring		£4500	£4700	£5000
Summer		£3800	£4000	£4100
Autumn	£5600	£6200	£6500	

  a Plot the data on a time series graph.

  b Describe the trend shown by the graph.

4 A beach café is open all year round. The table shows its quarterly sales figures, to the nearest £100, for three years.

	Jan–Mar	Apr–June	July–Sept	Oct–Dec
2007	£4000	£6200	£10 000	£5300
2008	£4200	£6500	£12 400	£4700
2009	£4000	£6600	£15 000	£5400

  a Plot the data on a time series graph.

  b Describe the trend shown by the graph.

  c One winter was particularly cold. Which winter do you think that is, and why?

Calculating with fractions and rounding (CN1)

You should know how to calculate a fraction of an amount.

a Akhtar and Ruby raise £360 for charity.

Akhtar raises $\dfrac{7}{12}$ of the money. How much does Ruby raise?

b Karen has 350 fliers to deliver. After 2 hours she has delivered 105 of them. What fraction of the fliers has she delivered?

a $\dfrac{5}{12} \times \dfrac{360}{1} = \dfrac{5 \times 360}{12} = £150$

b $\dfrac{105}{350} = \dfrac{21}{70} = \dfrac{3}{10}$

> You can enter fractions on your calculator. Some calculators have this key: $a^{b}/_{c}$

You can use either a written or a calculator method to add, subtract, multiply or divide fractions.

a Brian, Jenny and Sean share the cost of a meal. Brian ate most and pays $\dfrac{9}{20}$ of the bill, and Jenny pays $\dfrac{2}{5}$ of the bill.

What fraction of the bill does Sean pay?

b Show that $25 \div 10$ is the same as $\dfrac{1}{10}$ of 25.

Sheraton *Restaurant*
Emwell street, Warminster.

1 Chilli con carne & rice	xxxx
1 Roast chicken with potatoes	xxxx
1 Mushroom Pizza	xxxx
1 Jelly Yoghurt Fruit salad	xxxx
Total charges	**xxxx**

Thank You!

a $\dfrac{9}{20} + \dfrac{2}{5} = \dfrac{9}{20} + \dfrac{8}{20} = \dfrac{17}{20}$

Sean pays $1 - \dfrac{17}{20} = \dfrac{3}{20}$

b $25 \div 10 = 2.5$ $\dfrac{1}{10} \times 25 = \dfrac{25}{10} = 2.5.$

They are the same.

> Multiply $\dfrac{2}{5}$ by $\dfrac{4}{4}$ to get a common denominator.
> OR
> Enter on your calculator and add.

> "of" is the same as × using fractions.

You should also be prepared for **mixed numbers** (containing both an integer and a fraction part), such as $1\dfrac{1}{2}$. To multiply or divide mixed numbers, follow these steps.

Step 1 Change each mixed number to a "top heavy" fraction.
Step 2 Multiply or divide in the usual way.
Step 3 Cancel and turn the answer back to a mixed number.

$2\dfrac{2}{3} \times 1\dfrac{4}{5} = \dfrac{8}{3} \times \dfrac{9}{5} = \dfrac{72}{15} = \dfrac{24}{5} = 4\dfrac{4}{5}$

$2\dfrac{3}{4} \div 4\dfrac{1}{8} = \dfrac{11}{4} \div \dfrac{33}{8} = \dfrac{11}{4} \times \dfrac{8}{33} = \dfrac{88}{132} = \dfrac{2}{3}$

$= \dfrac{\cancel{11}}{\cancel{4}} \times \dfrac{\cancel{8}}{\cancel{33}} = \dfrac{2}{3}$

> Enter $2\dfrac{2}{3}$ using the fraction key on your calculator.
> This may be

> You could cancel 4 and 8, 11 and 33 to make numbers easier.

Exercise CN1

MEDIUM

1   In a Lucky Dip, tickets are only red, green or yellow.

Of the tickets, $\frac{2}{5}$ are red and $\frac{1}{3}$ are green.

What fraction of the tickets is yellow?

2   Tina manages a hotel that has 54 rooms.

One day 36 of the rooms have people staying in them.

   a   What fraction of the rooms in the hotel is **empty**?

   b   A third of all the hotel rooms are "Superior" and cost £104 a night.

   The rest are "Standard" and cost £80 a night.

   The same fraction of each type of room is empty.

   How much money will the hotel lose that day through rooms being empty?

3   Habib has to paint one side of a wall that is 4 m high and 25 m long.

He can paint 30 m² of the wall in a day.

   a   How many days will it take him to paint the wall?

   b   After $2\frac{1}{2}$ days, how many square metres of the wall does he still have to paint?

   c   What fraction of the wall has he painted after two days?

4   Complete these calculations.

   a $\frac{2}{3} - \frac{2}{5}$ **b** $\frac{1}{6} \times \frac{2}{5}$ **c** $\frac{2}{3} \div \frac{2}{9}$ **d** $\frac{3}{4} + \frac{1}{5}$

   e $\frac{1}{2} + \frac{5}{12}$ **f** $\frac{5}{6} \times \frac{2}{3}$ **g** $2\frac{1}{3} - 1\frac{4}{5}$ **h** $1\frac{2}{5} \times 2\frac{2}{7}$

   i $3\frac{2}{3} \div \frac{5}{6}$ **j** $4\frac{2}{5} \times 2\frac{1}{2}$ **k** $3\frac{2}{7} - \frac{2}{5}$ **l** $2\frac{4}{7} \div 1\frac{4}{5}$

5   Alan calculates $15 \times \frac{2}{3}$ and gets the answer $\frac{30}{45}$.

What mistake has he made and what is the correct answer?

6   Regan calculates $2\frac{4}{5} \times \frac{2}{7}$. This is her working:

$2 \times \frac{2}{7} + \frac{4}{5} \times \frac{2}{7} = \frac{4}{7} + \frac{8}{35} = \frac{20}{35} + \frac{8}{35} = \frac{28}{35}$

Does her method give the right answer?

Explain your answer.

7   Colin uses $\frac{4}{7}$ of a jar of marmalade in a week.

Will 29 jars be sufficient for Colin, at this rate, for a year?

8   A garden is $5\frac{3}{4}$ m long and $3\frac{2}{5}$ m wide.

Calculate its area and perimeter, writing your answers as fractions.

UNIT C

Calculator display and accuracy CN2

You should know how to round a calculator display to a number of **significant figures**. The first significant figure is the first digit from the left that is not 0.

    23 460 to 3sf ≈ 23 500

0.003516 to 2sf ≈ 0.0035

You should only round a number when you finish a calculation.

> *sf is an abbreviation for significant figures.*

EXAMPLE

a A merchant pays £23.37 for 9 identical bags of grain. How much would he pay for 16 bags?

b A lift can carry a maximum of 5 people. 36 people want to go to floor 27. How many trips will the lift make?

> **← LOOK BACK**
> See topic AN2 on page 4 to further revise rounding.

....

a 1 bag costs £23.37 ÷ 9 = £25966 …
16 bags cost £2.5966... × 16 = £41.5466 … or £41.55

b 36 ÷ 5 = 7.2   The lift will make 8 trips.

> *It would be wrong to round 7.2 down. Always look at the context of the problem.*

An instrument is only as **accurate** as the scale marked on it.

The length g of any line that is measured as 35 cm could be anything between 34.5 and 35.5 cm. So $34.5 \leq g < 35.5$

Measurement gives an **error** of 0.5 cm either way from 35 cm (±0.5 cm).

35.5 is the **upper bound (UB)** of g and 34.5 is the **lower bound (LB)** of g.

    34   34.5   35   35.5

This table tells you what bounds to use in calculations.

Operation	To find the upper bound	To find the lower bound
+	$UB_1 + UB_2$	$LB_1 + LB_2$
−	$UB_1 - LB_2$	$LB_1 - UB_2$
×	$UB_1 \times UB_2$	$LB_1 \times LB_2$
÷	$UB_1 \div LB_2$	$LB_1 \div UB_2$

> *UB_1 means "upper bound of measurement 1".*

EXAMPLE

a A boy is weighed as 64 kg, correct to the nearest kg. What is his least possible weight?

b A greetings card is 15 cm long, correct to the nearest cm. An envelope is 14.5 cm long correct to the nearest mm. Explain whether the card could ever fit into the envelope.

c Tony completes the 100 m race (measured to the nearest m) in 11.5 s (measured to 0.5 s). Find Tony's greatest possible speed in m/s.

....

a 63.5 kg.

> *There is an "error" of 0.5 kg, so 64 − 0.5 = 63.5*

b The card, recorded as 15 cm, could be as long as 15.5 cm.
The envelope, recorded as 145 mm, could be as short as 144.5 mm (or 14.45 cm).
So the card could be shorter than the envelope and so fit inside it.

c Speed $= \dfrac{\text{maximum distance}}{\text{minimum time}} = \dfrac{100.5}{11.25} = 8.9\dot{3}$ m/s

> *As the time is to the nearest 0.5 s, the possible error is half of this = 0.25 s*

Exercise CN2

1 Neil makes 2.75 kg of jam.

He puts the jam into glass jars that contain a maximum of 350 g.

a How many jars can he fill with the jam?

Neil plans to sell the jam. He buys a pack of 10 glass jars for £3.

The ingredients for the jam cost him £7.85 altogether.

b For how much should he sell each jar of jam so that he will make a profit?

2 Round each of these numbers to the required number of significant figures.

    a 3.406 84 to 1sf   **b** 3.406 84 to 3sf   **c** 13.417 to 2sf

    d 17 406.1 to 3sf   **e** 0.004 39 to 2sf   **f** 0.000 003 998 6 to 2sf

3 Electricity is sold at a price of 14.824p per unit of electricity.

Shona uses an average of 5.8 units each day in June.

How much does this electricity cost her?

4 A fish is weighed as 2.5 kg, correct to the nearest 100 g.

What are the upper and lower boundaries of the fish's weight?

5 Kira swims a length of the pool in 12 seconds correct to the nearest second.

Bart swims 10 lengths in a time of 2 minutes, correct to the nearest minute.

Is it certain that Kira is faster than Bart?

6 The world's tallest building, the Burj Khalifa in Dubai, is 828 metres tall.

It is not clear whether this is exact or rounded to some unit.

a Show the different maximum heights this could have if the measurement is rounded

    i to the nearest m   **ii** to the nearest half m   **iii** to the nearest cm.

b Which rounding records the greatest height for the building?

7 A garden is measured, correct to the nearest metre,
as 9 m by 6 m.

The whole garden is to be treated with fertiliser at a cost of £12.60 per square metre.

Find the maximum and minimum cost of treating the garden.

8 In triangle *ABC*, *AB* = 3 cm and *AC* = 12 cm each to the nearest cm.

Calculate the minimum size of angle ACB.

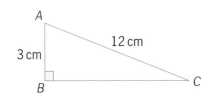

9 Karen cycles at a steady 18.5 km/h, to 1dp, for 75 minutes, to the nearest minute.

Calculate the upper and lower bounds of the distance she could have cycled.

Calculator skills and formulae

On a calculator, negative numbers are often entered using the (−) key.
You should put brackets around negative numbers in a formula.

EXAMPLE

a Find the value of $\sqrt[3]{32 + (-5.1)^2}$ and give your answer to 2sf.

b The formula for the volume of a cone is $V = \dfrac{\pi r^2 h}{3}$.
Find the volume of a cone, in m^3, with $r = 45\,cm$ and $h = 1.2\,m$.

> The first bracket after $\sqrt{}$ appears automatically for some calculators.

a $\boxed{\sqrt[3]{}}\ \boxed{(}\ \boxed{32}\ \boxed{+}\ \boxed{(}\ \boxed{(-)}\ \boxed{5.1}\ \boxed{)}\ \boxed{x^2}\ \boxed{)} = 3.8710990... \approx 3.9$ to 2sf

b $V = \dfrac{\pi \times 0.45^2 \times 1.2}{3}$

> Change cm to m

> Always write more than 2sf and then round the answer.

$= \boxed{(}\ \boxed{\pi}\ \boxed{\times}\ \boxed{.45}\ \boxed{x^2}\ \boxed{\times}\ \boxed{1.2}\ \boxed{)}\ \boxed{\div}\ \boxed{3} = 0.254469... \approx 0.25$ to 2sf

> Use the π key or 3.142

> The information is given to 2sf so it is sensible to round the answer to 2sf.

You should also be careful when entering negative values into an equation.

EXAMPLE

Complete the table of values for $y = 3x^2 - 2x$.

x	−3	−2	−1	0
$3x^2 - 2x$		16		0

When $x = -3$, $3x^2 - 2x = 3 \times (-3)^2 - 2 \times -3 = 33$
When $x = -1$, $3x^2 - 2x = 3 \times (-1)^2 - 2 \times -1 = 5$

Calculator skills are very useful in trigonometry problems.

EXAMPLE

Find angle C when $\cos C = \dfrac{3.5^2 + 4.2^2 - 2.9^2}{2 \times 3.5 \times 4.2}$.

> See the sine and cosine rule on page 136.

$\boxed{(}\ \boxed{3.5}\ \boxed{x^2}\ \boxed{+}\ \boxed{4.2}\ \boxed{x^2}\ \boxed{-}\ \boxed{2.9}\ \boxed{x^2}\ \boxed{)}$
$\boxed{\div}\ \boxed{(}\ \boxed{2}\ \boxed{\times}\ \boxed{3.5}\ \boxed{\times}\ \boxed{4.2}\ \boxed{)} = 0.73061...$
$\boxed{\text{shift}}\ \boxed{\cos}\ \boxed{\text{Ans}}\ \boxed{=}\ 43.0622... \rightarrow 43°$ to 2sf.

You can also use a calculator with percentage problems.

EXAMPLE

The price of a car in a sale is £14 440.
This is the price after a reduction of 5%.
By how much has the price of the car been reduced?

The original price is reduced by 5% so £14 440 is 95% of the original price.

(Price $\times 0.95 = £14\,440$)

Price $= \dfrac{£14\,440}{0.95} = £15\,200$

Exercise CN3

1 Calculate the value of each of these.
   Give each answer correct to 3sf.

   a $\dfrac{4.5 - 2.7}{3.2}$

   b $\sqrt{3.2^2 + 1.7^2}$

   c $\dfrac{\sqrt{37.9}}{2.4^2}$

   d $\dfrac{12.7 - 3.6^2}{2.1 + 5}$

   e $\sqrt[3]{63.3 - 2.4^2}$

   f $32.4 - \dfrac{127}{2.3^2}$

   g $-4.5^3 + \sqrt{27}$

   h $\left(\dfrac{2}{1.3^3}\right)^2$

2 The area of a circle may be found using the formula $A = \pi r^2$.
   Calculate the area of a circle when $r = 39\,$mm.
   Give your answer in cm².

3 Copy and complete this table of values for $y = 5x^2 - x$.

x	−3	−2	−1	0	1
$5x^2 - x$	48			0	

4 The time it takes for a pendulum to complete one
   swing may be found using the formula

   $$T = 2\pi\sqrt{\dfrac{l}{g}}.$$

   Find the time for a pendulum to complete one swing when $l = 13.7$ and $g = 10.8$.

5 Find the values of these expressions.

   a $x^3 - 2$ when $x = 5.1$

   b $\dfrac{a + ab}{6}$ when $a = 5$ and $b = -2$

   c $\sqrt{p^2 - q^2}$ when $p = 13.2$ and $q = 1.6$

   d $\dfrac{\pi r^2 h}{3}$ when $r = 4.5\,$cm and $h = 12\,$mm

6 Find the original value in each case.
   a New price £54 after reduction of 10%
   b New price £81.60 after reduction of 15%
   c New length 58.8 cm after increase of 5%
   d New area 114 m² after increase of 50%

7 Calculate the value of

   a $\dfrac{8 \times \cos 56°}{\sin 84°}$

   b $\dfrac{7.1^2 - (5.6 \cos 40°)^2}{2.3 \sin 70°}$

   c $\sqrt{\left(\dfrac{5.1^2 + 3.6^2}{\sin 56°}\right)}$

   d $\dfrac{-16 + \sqrt{16^2 - 4 \times 3 \times 2.5}}{2 \times 3}$

8 Brian's new quote for his car insurance is £460.
   Brian says: "Wow, that's up more than 15% on last year".
   What is the highest price Brian could have paid for his insurance last year?

Standard index form

Standard index form is used to write very large and very small numbers.

For example, 3×10^7 or 2.5×10^{-5}

- Standard index form is **always** written

$$a \times 10^b$$

$1 \le a < 10$ ⟶   ⟵ b is an integer

You can convert between standard index form and ordinary numbers.

Many calculators have a key to enter standard index form numbers, often **EXP** or **EE**.

So 1.45×10^8 can be entered using the key press sequence:

$1.45 \rightarrow$ **EXP** $\rightarrow 8$

The display will give you the "ordinary number" 145 000 000.

EXAMPLE

1 Write these numbers in standard index form.

   a   125 000 000 000   **b**   0.000 000 169

2 Write **a** 1.305×10^{-15} and   **b** 9.09×10^2 as ordinary numbers.

....

1 Count the number of digits the decimal point needs to move to make a number between 1 and 10:

   a   125 000 000 000 $= 1.25 \times 10^{11}$

   b   0.000 000 169 $= 1.69 \times 10^{-7}$

2 **a** $a = 1.305$, $b = -15$ Write 1.305 and move the decimal point **left** 15 places.

                                              0.000 000 000 000 001 305

   b $a = 9.09$, $b = 2$ Write 9.09 and move the decimal point **right** 2 places.

                                                909

You can calculate with standard index form and solve real-life problems.

EXAMPLE

1 Work out   **a** $(3.2 \times 10^4) \times (5.6 \times 10^3)$ **b** $(4.52 \times 10^7) \div (6.8 \times 10^{-3})$

   Write your answers correct to 2sf.

2 There are roughly 7×10^{27} atoms in an adult human being and 6.85×10^9 human beings alive in the world today.

   a   Calculate an estimate for the number of atoms in all the human beings alive today.

   b   Explain why this is an estimate.

3 The speed of light is approximately 3.0×10^8 m/s.

   Alpha Centauri is 4.134×10^{13} km from our Sun.

   How many seconds will it take light to travel between the Sun and Alpha Centauri?

....

1 **a** $3.2 \rightarrow$ **EXP** $\rightarrow 4 \rightarrow \times \rightarrow 5.6 \rightarrow$ **EXP** $\rightarrow 3 \rightarrow = 179\ 200\ 000 = 1.8 \times 10^8$

   b $4.52 \rightarrow$ **EXP** $\rightarrow 7 \rightarrow \div \rightarrow 6.8 \rightarrow$ **EXP** $\rightarrow$ **(–)** $\rightarrow 3 \rightarrow = 6\ 647\ 058\ 824 = 6.6 \times 10^9$

2 **a** $7 \rightarrow$ **EXP** $\rightarrow 27 \rightarrow \times \rightarrow 6.85 \rightarrow$ **EXP** $\rightarrow 9 \rightarrow = 4.795 \times 10^{37}$

   b   The number of atoms in each human and the world population are both estimates.

3   4.134×10^{13} km $\times 1000 = 4.134 \times 10^{16}$ m

     $4.134 \times 10^{16} \div (3.0 \times 10^8) = 137\ 800\ 000$ seconds or 1.378×10^8 s

     (This is 1594 days 21 hours 46 minutes and 40 seconds.)

Exercise CN4

1 Write each of these numbers in standard index form.
   Round each number to 3sf.
   a 479.2   b 0.003829   c 125 698 000   d −150.348
   e 0.001 032 59   f 685 008 600 045 g 87.0003   h 3.5097

2 Write each of these standard index form numbers as ordinary numbers.
   a 2.67×10^4 b 3.14×10^{14} c 9.34×10^{-4} d 1.08×10^{-8}
   e 1.20×10^{-10} f 2.07×10^8 g 6.619×10^5 h 2.016×10^{-12}

3 Calculate each of these and write your answer in standard form.
   a $(1.75 \times 10^5) \times (9.02 \times 10^6)$ b $(3.05 \times 10^{15}) \div (5.11 \times 10^8)$
   c $(3.1 \times 10^{12}) + (1.26 \times 10^4)$ d $(2.011 \times 10^{-2}) \times (4.16 \times 10^5)$
   e $(2 \times 10^{15}) - (7.32 \times 10^6)$ f $(3 \times 10^5) \times (9 \times 10^6) \times (8 \times 10^{-3})$
   g $\dfrac{2.59 \times 10^{12}}{1.14 \times 10^9}$ h $(2.68 \times 10^{-6})^3$

   i $\sqrt{\dfrac{5.6 \times 10^8}{3 \times 10^{-3}}}$ j $(6.9 \times 10^{15}) + (1.2 \times 10^5) \times (5.9 \times 10^{-4})$

4 The average radius of the earth is 6.371×10^3 km.
   The earth may be modelled as a sphere.
   The volume of a sphere may be calculated using the formula $V = \dfrac{4 \pi r^3}{3}$.   ← | 1 000 000 g = 1 tonne
                                                                                              | 100 cm = 1 m
                                                                                              | 1000 m = 1 km
   a Calculate the volume of the earth in km³.

   The mean density of the earth is 5.5 g/cm³ correct to 2sf.
   b Calculate an estimate of the mass of the earth in tonnes.

5 The diameters of atoms range from 1×10^{-10} m to 5×10^{-10} m (0.1 to 0.5 nanometres).
   If the 7×10^{27} atoms in an adult human being were arranged side by side,
   how long could the arrangement of atoms be? Explain your answer.

6 A cement lorry can carry 1.08×10^4 kg of concrete.
   The CN tower in Canada was built using 4.05×10^4 m³ of concrete.
   1 m³ of concrete weighs 2.4 tonnes.
   a What weight of concrete was used to build the CN tower?
   b How many lorry loads of concrete would be required to build the CN tower?

7 The Caspian Sea is the largest inland lake in the world.
   It contains 7.87×10^4 km³ of water.
   a How many m³ of water does the Caspian Sea contain?
   b Given the following information,   1 m³ = 264.17 gallons,
                                           1 kg = 2.2046 lb, (lb = pounds)
                                           1 gallon of salt water weighs 8.556 lb
   what is the mass of water in the Caspian Sea?
   Give your answer in kilograms.

Percentage problems

		Step 1		Step 2		Step 3
To **increase** amount **Q** by **P**%	→	Add **P** to 100	→	divide by 100	→	multiply by **Q**.
To **decrease** amount **Q** by **P**%	→	Take **P** from 100	→	divide by 100	→	multiply by **Q**.
To find an original amount after an increase of **P**% to **Q**	→	Add **P** to 100	→	divide by 100	→	divide **Q** by the result
To find an original amount after a decrease of **P**% to **Q**	→	Take **P** from 100	→	divide by 100	→	divide **Q** by the result

You can use these methods to repeatedly change an amount by a percentage.

EXAMPLE

A plant grows in height by 23% each year.
At the end of a year it is 85 cm high.
Find its height after 4 more years.

Step 1   100 + 23 = 123
Step 2   123 ÷ 100 = 1.23
Step 3   85 × 1.23 × 1.23 × 1.23 × 1.23 =
            194.55364... = 194.6 cm to 1 dp.

← LOOK BACK
See topic AN1 on page 2 to revise multiplying and dividing by power of 10.

1.23 × 1.23 × 1.23 × 1.23 is the same as 1.23⁴

Do this on the calculator as 1.23 4

This is **much** quicker than finding 23%, adding it on then finding another 23% etc.

EXAMPLE

a   Find 27% of 2.39 m correct to 2 dp.
b   Barry's weekly train fare increases by 11.5%.
    He used to pay £35.60 a week.
    Calculate the cost of his new weekly fare.
c   Chloe has £2300 to invest.
    Her bank offers her 4.5% interest each year, which will be added to her savings.
    How much will Chloe's savings be worth at the end of five years and how much interest will she have?
d   Rory buys a pair of trainers for £85 but they rub his feet.
    He sells them for £70.
    What is his percentage loss?
e   After a general election Jonah hears on the news that the number of people voting in his town has dropped by 24% since the previous election, and that only 19 456 people voted. How many people voted in the last election?

This is called **compound interest**.

It is a good idea to write £ in the calculation to help you remember the units (£) for the answer.
Round to the nearest penny.

a   0.27 × 2.39 m = 0.6453 = 0.65 m to 2dp
b   1.115 × £35.60 = £39.694 = £39.69
c   1.045⁵ × £2300 = £2866.2184... = £2866.22
    She earned   £2866.22 − 2300 = £566.22 interest.
d   15 ÷ 85 × 100 = 17.647... = 17.6% to 1dp
e   19456 ÷ 0.76 = 25 600

He loses £15 so he has lost $\frac{15}{85}$ of the money he spent.
Always divide by the original amount.

19 456 is only 100 − 24 = 76% of those who voted before.
76% = 0.76 so divide by 0.76 (this is like dividing by 76 to find 1% then × 100 for 100%)

Exercise CN5

1 Calculate
   a 25% of £24.60
   b 7% of 42 km
   c 11% of 12 kg
   d 17.5% of 49.8 m
   e 22.5% of 8 hours
   f 1% of 46p

2 A design has an area of 150 cm². It is photocopied and the area is enlarged by 12%.
   What is the area of the enlarged design?

3 Sally bought an old bike for £32. She repaired it and sold it for £44.
   What was her percentage profit?

4 Karen's salary, before any deductions, is £1455 a month. She is given a pay rise of 7.5%.
   a Calculate her new monthly pay.
   b Karen has 17% of her salary deducted for tax.
     Calculate how much money Karen is actually paid after her payrise.

5 For an average man aged between 17 and 29, 8% of body weight is fat.
   a Tony weighs 75 kg on his 28th birthday.
     Calculate how much of Tony's weight is fat.
   b Tony is not very fit and gains weight by 5% each year.
     Calculate Tony's possible body weight on his 35th birthday.
   c Explain why he may not weigh this amount on his 35th birthday.

6 The value of a car decreases at the rate of 15% each year for the first three years.
   A new car is bought for £10 500. Calculate the value of the car after three years.

7 A rectangle has sides of 25 cm and 18 cm. The length is reduced by
   20% and the width increased by 10%.
   a Calculate the area of the reduced rectangle.
   b What percentage of the original area is the new area?
   c By what percentage has the original area been reduced?

8 At the start of 2010 the average house price was £224 000.
   It is predicted that house prices will rise by 2% each year.
   a What will the average house price be at the start of 2020?
   b Explain why this may not be the average house price in 2020.
   c In what year could the price of an average house be more than £1 m?

9 Joan has £2600 to invest.
   Joan is offered these two options:
   a buy a bond that pays 4.8% compound interest each year but
     she cannot take out any of the money until five years have passed
   b have a savings account that pays 5% of £2600 each year.
   Which option would you recommend to Joan and why would you recommend it?

10 A car lost 10% of its value each year for the first five years.
   It then lost 5% of its value for the next five years until its value is £7500.
   What was the original value of the car?

You can use **proportion** in problems where amounts are scaled up or down by multiplying or dividing.

a Choco Pops costs £1.75 for 350 g. Choc Rice costs £1.90 for 400 g. Which cereal is better "value for money"?

b It is reckoned that it took four monks five years to copy an ancient manuscript.
How long would it have taken
   i   one monk?   **ii**   ten monks?

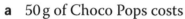

---

a 50 g of Choco Pops costs   175p ÷ 7 = 25p
50 g of Choc Rice costs   190p ÷ 8 = 23.75p
Choc Rice is better value.

b **i**   4 × 5 = 20 years   longer so multiply
   ii   20 ÷ 10 = 2 years   shorter so divide

Two quantities, a and b, may be related by different types of proportion.

Statement	Statement in symbols	Proportion equation
a is proportional to b	$a \propto b$	$a = kb$
a is proportional to $\sqrt{b}$	$a \propto \sqrt{b}$	$a = k\sqrt{b}$
a is proportional to b^n	$a \propto b^n$	$a = kb^n$
a is inversely proportional to b	$a \propto \dfrac{1}{b}$	$a = \dfrac{k}{b}$
a is inversely proportional to $\sqrt{b}$	$a \propto \dfrac{1}{\sqrt{b}}$	$a = \dfrac{k}{\sqrt{b}}$
a is inversely proportional to b^n	$a \propto \dfrac{1}{b^n}$	$a = \dfrac{k}{b^n}$

In **direct proportion**, both sets of values increase together.

In **inverse proportion**, one set increases as the other decreases.

All proportion problems can be solved using a similar method.
Start by writing the proportion equation and then find k.

You can **check** your equation is correct by substituting the known values:

$8 = 0.5 \times 4^2$ true

$5 = 40 \div 8$ true

a a is directly proportional to b^2.
When a is 8, b is 4.
Find the value of b when a is 72.

First find the equation:

$a = kb^2$

$8 = k \times 16$

$\dfrac{8}{16} = k = 0.5$

$a = 0.5b^2$

Then answer the question:

$72 = 0.5b^2$

$72 \div 0.5 = b^2$

$144 = b^2$

$12 = b$

b a is inversely proportional to b.
When a is 5, b is 8.
Find the value of a when b is 2.

First find the equation:

$a = \dfrac{k}{b}$

$5 = \dfrac{k}{8}$

$40 = k$

$a = \dfrac{40}{b}$

Then answer the question:

$a = \dfrac{40}{b}$

$a = \dfrac{40}{2}$

$a = 20$

HIGH

1 Brian walks 10 km in four hours. How far will
   he walk in 10 hours?

2 One portion of cereal, weighing 30 g, contains 173 kcal.
   The recommended daily amount for a woman is 2000 kcal.
   A box contains 375 g of cereal. Tina ate half the box of cereal.
   Has she eaten her recommended daily amount of kcal?

3 These are some of the ingredients for making 10 chocolate muffins.

   > 115 g butter
   > 70 g caster sugar
   > 2 eggs
   > 215 g plain flour

   a How much of each ingredient would you need to
      make 25 of these muffins?
   b Why would it be difficult to make a number
      of muffins that was not a multiple of 5, using this recipe?

4 It takes five workers six hours to harvest a field.
   One worker hurts his back and has to go home.
   How long will it take the remaining workers to harvest the next
   field, which is twice as big as the last one?

5 Two sets of values, *a* and *b*, are directly related.
   When $a = 10$, $b = 25$. Find the value of *b* when $a = 28$.

6 Two sets of values, *a* and *b*, are inversely proportional.
   When $a = 20$, $b = 6$. Find the value of *b* when $a = 15$.

7 *p* is inversely proportional to q^2. When $p = 10$, $q = 2$.
   a Find the value of *p* when $q = 8$.
   b Find the value of *q* when $p = 64$.

8 *p* is proportional to $\sqrt{q}$. When $p = 10$, $q = 2$.
   a Find the value of *p* when $q = 25$.
   b Find the value of *q* when $p = 40$.

9 As a light source is moved away from a screen the intensity
   of the light decreases.
   The intensity, *I*, is inversely proportional to the square of the
   distance, *d*, from the screen.
   a Find the formula relating *I* and *d*, if $I = 0.12$ lux and $d = 10$ cm.
   b Find *I*, if the same light source is moved so that it is 20 cm from the screen.

10 A swimming pool is filled in 21 hours by 5 pumps supplying water at a constant rate.
   An extra pump is brought to speed up the process. It supplies water at the same rate
   as the other pumps. How much time is saved by using 6 pumps instead of 5?

UNIT C

Compound measures

Compound measures involve two units, for example
- **Speed**   measured in mph or miles per hour   (the distance you travel in one hour)
- **Density**   measured in g/cm³ or grams per cm³   (the weight of one cm³ of the material)

The units of density are g/cm³.

g is a measure of **mass**, cm³ is a measure of **volume** and / is divide.

So density = $\dfrac{mass}{volume}$

You can use "cover up" in this triangle to turn this into three formulae.

So   density = $\dfrac{mass}{volume}$ volume = $\dfrac{mass}{density}$

and   mass = density × volume

EXAMPLE

a   Brian cycles at a steady speed of 12 km/h.
How far will he cycle in 45 minutes?

b   Maryann is paid £15.30 per hour.
For how long will she have to work to earn £210?

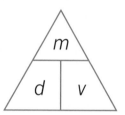

c   At the end of 2008:
The UK had a population of 6.1414×10^7. The area of the UK is 2.4482×10^5 square miles.
China had a population of 1.321×10^9. The area of China is 2.4576×10^7 square miles.
Which country was the more densely populated at the end of 2008?

d   Dain is paid 45p to address 10 envelopes.
It takes him 5 minutes to address 15 envelopes.
If Dain works at the same pace for 3 hours, how much money will he earn?

. . . .

a   You are asked for distance:

$d = s \times t = 12 \times \dfrac{3}{4} = 9\,\text{km}.$ ←   45 minutes = $\dfrac{3}{4}$ h

b   210 ÷ 15.3 = 13.725... hrs
Maryann will have to work for 14 hours.   ←   She can only work 13 or 14, and 13 is not enough!

c   Population density = $\dfrac{population}{area}$

UK   = $\dfrac{61\,414\,000 \text{ people}}{244\,820 \text{ miles}^2}$ = $2.50853... \times 10^2 \approx 251$ people per square mile.

China   = $\dfrac{1\,321\,000\,000 \text{ people}}{24\,576\,000 \text{ miles}^2}$ = $53.75... \times 10^1 \approx 54$ people per square mile.

The UK was more densely populated (roughly 5 times greater than China).

d   In 1 hour   60 ÷ 5 = 12 lots of 15 envelopes
                            = 180 envelopes

In 3 hours   = 180 × 3 = 540 envelopes.
            540 ÷ 10 = 54 lots of 10 envelopes

Dain is paid 54 × 45p = 2430p   ←   Keep pence in the calculation to avoid silly answers like £2430.
                    = £24.30 in 3 hours.

Exercise CN7

1 What is the average speed of a cyclist who travels 30 km in 1½ hours?

2 A car travels for 1 hour 35 minutes at a steady speed of 60 km/h.
How many kilometres has the car travelled?

3 Sue walks from home to the shops and back at a steady 3 mph.
The shops are 2 miles from home.
How many minutes does the walk take Sue?

4 Silver has a density of 1.05×10^1 gm/cm³. A silver bracelet weighs 2.0×10^2 g.
 a How many cm³ of silver have been used to make the bracelet?

 The cost of the silver used to make the bracelet is £1762.
 b What is the cost of 1 g of silver?

5 The cost of sending a single text message is 12p.
However, you can buy a package of 30 messages at £3 per month.
Give an example to show the following.
 • Someone who is better off sending single text messages.
 • Someone who is better off buying a package of messages.

6 A Cape Hunting Dog can run at a speed of 45 mph.
At this speed, how far will it run in 40 seconds?

7 Bangladesh has a population density of 2.9×10^3 people per square mile and a population of 1.62×10^8.
What is the approximate area of Bangladesh?
Remember to state your units and round your answer sensibly.

8 Colin cleans windows. He uses this information to estimate his income.

Large house	1 house every 18 minutes	
Average house	1 house every 8 minutes	£12
Small house	1 house every 6 minutes	

 How much should he charge for each other type of house?

9 A photocopier will print 1.1×10^2 copies per minute.
How long will it take to print 20 documents each containing 4.4×10^2 pages?

10 Water from a tap flows at a rate of 12.5 cm³ per second.
The tap fills a container in 11.6 seconds.
 a What is the volume of the container?
 b The same tap fills another container in 0.5 minutes.
  What is the volume of this container?
 c The same tap is used to fill a 1 litre container.
  How many minutes will it take to do this?

UNIT C

Many quantities change **exponentially** over time.

The formula for two variables (x and y) in an exponential relationship is

$$y = A \times b^x$$

A is the initial value

If b is greater than 1, there is growth.
If b is less than 1, there is decay.

Compound interest is an example of **exponential growth**.

Depreciation is an example of **exponential decay**.

What would £4500 (A), invested at 5% interest per year for 10 years (x), be worth (y)?

$y = 4500 \times 1.05^{10} = £7330.03$

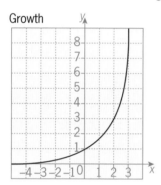

What would a car costing £12 600 (A), that depreciates at 5% per year, be worth (y) after 10 years (x)?

$y = 12\,600 \times 0.95^{10} = £7544.09$

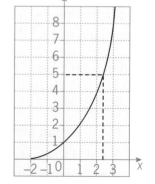

Here are the characteristic graph shapes of exponential growth and decay.

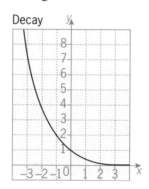

EXAMPLE

a Draw the graph of $y = 2^x$ for values of x from -2 to 3.
   Use your graph to solve the equation $2^x = 5$.

b A species of algae covers $12\,\text{m}^2$ of the surface of a lake. The algae are growing at a rate of 15% per day. What area do the algae cover after eight days?

c Thorium decays at a rate of 2.8% each day.
   How many days will it take for 60 g of thorium to decay to half of its weight?

a

x	-2	-1	0	1	2	3
2^x	0.25	0.5	1	2	4	8

To solve $2^x = 5$ draw the line $y = 5$ to meet the graph line and read off:
$x = 2.3$ to 1 dp

Check that $2^{2.3} \approx 5$ ($2^{2.3} = 4.92457...$)

b $12 \times 1.15^8 = 36.7\,\text{m}^2$ to 3sf

c Solve $60 \times 0.972^x = 30$ using trial and improvement.
   $0.972^x = 0.5$

   divide by 60

   $x = 10$: $0.972^{10} = 0.752...$ $x = 20$: $0.972^{20} = 0.566...$ $x = 25$: $0.972^{25} = 0.491...$

   $x = 24$: $0.972^{24} = 0.505...$ $x = 24.5$: $0.972^{24.5} = 0.498$ $x = 24.6$: $0.972^{24.4} = 0.500...$

   Answer 24.6 days

Exercise CN8

HIGH

1 £6800 is invested at 3.5% interest each year for 20 years.
What is its value at the end of that period?

2 Brian invests £17 000 in a savings bond that matures after eight years.
The rate of interest is 9%.
He thinks that he will double his investment.
Is Brian correct?

3 The number of a strain of bacteria decays exponentially
according to this formula
$$N = 500\ 000 \times 2^{-t}$$
where N is the number of bacteria at a given time
and t is the time, in hours.
  a **i** If $t = 0$, what is the value of N?
  ii What does this mean?
  b How many bacteria were present after 10 hours?
  c How many hours will it take until the number of bacteria
  falls below 1 and they cease to be present?

4 Draw the graph of $y = 0.5^x$ for values of x from -3 to 3.
  a Use your graph to solve the equation $0.5^x = 3$.
  b Show a check of your answer using your calculator.

5 A drug, injected into the blood stream, has a half-life of 24 hours.
If 140 mg is injected, find the amount remaining after four days.

> Half-life of 24 hours means only half of the drug will be present after 24 hours.

6 Radium decays at the very slow rate of 0.044% each year.
  a Show that radium has a half-life of between 1500 and 1600 years.
  b Find, to the nearest year, the half-life of radium.

7 A population of insect quadruples every day.
If there are 12 insects at the start of 1 June, how many will there
be at the start of July?
Give your answer in standard index form correct to 3 sf.

8 In March 2006 there were 26 208 000 cars on the roads of Britain.
This was a growth of 1.8% on the previous year.
  a How many cars had been on the roads of Britain in 2005?
  b If the rate of growth of the number of cars on the road continued
  at 1.8%, how many cars could be on the roads of Britain in 2020?

UNIT C

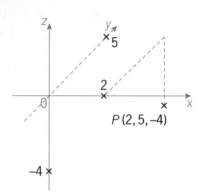

$P(2,5,-4)$

3D coordinates are used to represent points in space. The coordinate directions are x, y and z.

The point $P(5, 2, -4)$ is located $+5$ units in the x direction, $+2$ in the y direction, and -4 in the z direction.

EXAMPLE

The cuboid *OABCDEFG* has one vertex at the point $(5, 3, 2)$.

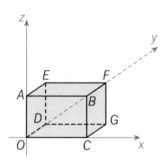

Write down the coordinates of
a point *A*   **b** point *G*   **c** the midpoint of *OF*

Looking at the diagram, the point *F* must be at $(5, 3, 2)$ because the other points would have at least one zero in their coordinates.
a *A* is $(0, 0, 2)$ **b** *G* is $(5, 3, 0)$
c the midpoint of $(0, 0, 0)$ and $(5, 3, 2)$ is $(2.5, 1.5, 1)$.

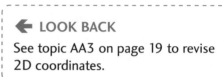

← **LOOK BACK**

See topic AA3 on page 19 to revise 2D coordinates.

To find the midpoint take the (mean) average for each of the three coordinates.

Exercise CA1

MEDIUM

1 An archeological dig is taking place in a field. The archaeologists use a coordinate system where each unit represents 1 metre on the 2D plan of the ground shown in the diagram, and also in the third dimension for height above/below ground.

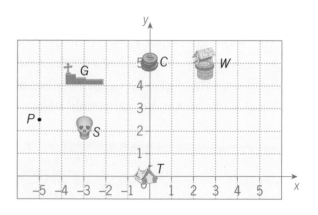

  a The flag on the tent, T, is 5 m high. Give the 3D coordinates of the flag.

  b The skull, S, is 1 m below ground level. Give the 3D coordinates of the skull.

  c The coins, C, are at ground level. Give the 3D coordinates of the coins.

  d The grave, G, is 2 m deep. Give the 3D coordinates of the centre of the base of the grave.

  e The well, W, is 18 m deep. Give the coordinates of the centre of bottom of the well.

  f A retaining rope is attached from the top of the flagpole to ground level at P. Give the 3D coordinates of the midpoint of the rope.

Trial and improvement

- **Trial and improvement** is a method of solving equations where there is no simple algebraic solution.

← **LOOK BACK**
See topic AA1 on page 16 to revise symbols and the meaning of 'equation', 'formula', 'identity' and expression.

EXAMPLE

a Show that the equation $x^3 - 2x = 15$ has a solution between 2 and 3.

A **trial** occurs when you substitute a value into the equation.

b Use trial and improvement to find this solution correct to 2 decimal places. Show all your **trials** and their outcomes.

a When $x = 2$, $x^3 - 2x = 2^3 - 2 \times 2$ When $x = 3$, $x^3 - 2x = 3^3 - 2 \times 3$
$$= 8 - 4 \qquad\qquad\qquad\qquad = 27 - 6$$
$$= 4 \qquad\qquad\qquad\qquad\quad = 21$$

Because the first value is **less** than 15 and the second is **greater** than 15, the solution must lie between these two values.

b Put your results in a table:

x	$x^3 - 2x$	Comment
2.4	9.024	Too small
2.7	14.283	Too small
2.8	16.352	Too big
2.73	14.886 417	Too small
2.74	15.090 824 0	Too big
2.735	14.988 415 4	Too small

It doesn't matter how many different values you try.

EXAMINER'S TIP

You **must** do the halfway value to confirm whether 2.73 or 2.74 is closest. Otherwise you will lose marks.

Because the solution lies between 2.735 and 2.74, $x = 2.74$ to 2 decimal places.

Exercise CA2

MEDIUM

1 Use trial and improvement to solve these equations, giving your answer correct to 1 decimal place.
   a $x^3 + x = 20$ **b** $2x^3 - x = 10$ **c** $4x - x^3 = -16$
   d $2^x = 11$ **e** $5^x = 20$ **f** $3^x = 0.8$

2 Use trial and improvement to solve these equations, giving your answer correct to 2 decimal places.
   a $x^3 - 5x = 5$ **b** $6^x + x = 30$ **c** $6x^2 - x^5 = 8$

3 A cuboid of volume $100\,\text{cm}^3$ has its length 1 cm more than its width and its height 1 cm more than its length. Its width is given by w.
   a Show that $3 < w < 4$.
   b Use trial and improvement to find w correct to 3 decimal places.

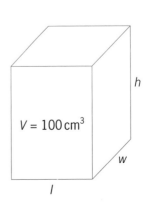

$V = 100\,\text{cm}^3$

Quadratic expressions

- You can **expand** two brackets by multiplying every term in one bracket by every term in the other bracket.

$(x + 6)(x - 3) = x^2 + 6x - 3x - 18$

A useful mnemonic is FOIL (firsts, outers, inners, lasts)

These are all **quadratic** expressions (x^2 is the highest power).

EXAMPLE

Expand and simplify

a $(x+2)(x+5)$ **b** $(w+5)(w-5)$ **c** $(2y-3)(3y+1)$ **d** $(2x+1)^2$

a $(x+2)(x+5) = x^2 + 5x + 2x + 10$
$$= x^2 + 7x + 10$$

b $(w+5)(w-5) = w^2 - 5w + 5w - 25$
$$= w^2 - 25$$

c $(2y-3)(3y+1) = 6y^2 + 2y - 9y - 3$
$$= 6y^2 - 7y - 3$$

d $(2x+1)^2 = (2x+1)(2x+1)$
$$= 4x^2 + 2x + 2x + 1$$
$$= 4x^2 + 4x + 1$$

Technically these are all **identities** so that
$(2x + 1)^2 \equiv 4x^2 + 4x + 1$

- **Factorising** is the opposite of expanding.
  You put an expression **into** brackets.

If there is no number before the x^2 term, then look for two numbers that multiply to give the number at the end and add to give the number before the x.

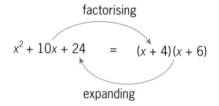

factorising

$x^2 + 10x + 24 \quad = \quad (x + 4)(x + 6)$

expanding

EXAMPLE

Factorise

a $x^2 + 10x + 16$ **b** $x^2 - x - 30$ **c** $x^2 - 36$

a $x^2 + 10x + 16 = (x + 8)(x + 2)$ **b** $x^2 - x - 30 = (x - 6)(x + 5)$ Remember that $-x$ means $-1x$.

$\qquad 10 = 8 + 2 \qquad 16 = 8 \times 2 \qquad\qquad -1 = -6 + 5 \qquad -30 = -6 \times 5$

c $x^2 - 36 = (x + 6)(x - 6)$ This form is called 'difference of two squares'.

If there **is** a number before the x^2 term, use trial and error to find the correct terms in each bracket.

EXAMPLE

Factorise   **a** $10x^2 - x - 3$ **b** $2x^3 - 8x$

a $10x^2 - x - 3 = (2x + 1)(5x - 3)$

$\qquad\qquad 10 = 2 \times 5 \qquad -3 = 1 \times -3$

b $2x^3 - 8x = 2x(x^2 - 4)$ taking out a common factor of $2x$
$$= 2x(x + 2)(x - 2) \quad \text{using the difference of two squares}$$

Remember *factorise* always means **factorise fully**.

Exercise CA3

MEDIUM HIGH

1 Expand and simplify

  a $(x+3)(x+8)$ **b** $(x+6)(x-9)$ **c** $(x-1)(x+10)$

  d $(x-5)(x-7)$ **e** $(x+7)^2$ **f** $(x-4)^2$

  g $(2x+3)(x+1)$ **h** $(2x-4)(3x+2)$ **i** $(x+7)(4x-5)$

  j $(3x-7)(5x-2)$ **k** $(2x+5)^2$ **l** $(3x-4)^2$

2 Expand and simplify

  a $(x+4)(x-5)+x(x-2)$ **b** $(x-5)(x-8)+(x+3)(x-6)$ **c** $(x-4)(x+9)-(x+6)(x-6)$

3 Factorise

  a $x^2+9x+20$ **b** $x^2+10x+21$ **c** x^2+7x+6

  d $x^2+14x+45$ **e** $x^2-3x-40$ **f** $x^2-5x-14$

  g $x^2-8x-33$ **h** x^2-x-42 **i** $x^2+2x-80$

  j $x^2+4x-12$ **k** $x^2+6x-72$ **l** x^2+x-72

  m x^2-2x+1 **n** $x^2-10x+24$ **o** $x^2-9x+20$

  p $x^2-20x+96$

4 Factorise

  a $2x^2+10x+12$ **b** $3x^2+9x+6$ **c** x^2-81

  d x^2-144 **e** x^2-9x **f** $4x^2-28x-72$

  g $x^2-\dfrac{1}{4}$ **h** x^2+12x **i** $4x^2-9$

  j x^3-3x^2 **k** $9x^2-\dfrac{16}{49}$ **l** $7x^2-28$

5 Factorise

  a $2x^2+9x+4$ **b** $6x^2+7x+2$ **c** $8x^2+6x-9$

  d $5x^2-17x-12$ **e** $6x^2-53x+40$ **f** $12x^2-x-6$

  g x^3+11x^2+18x **h** x^3-x^2-56x **i** $2x^3-18x$

  j $5x^2-\dfrac{5}{36}$ **k** $x^4-6x^3+9x^2$ **l** $3x^4-243x^2$

6 Find an expression for the shaded area.
All lengths are in cm.

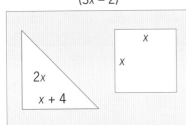

Algebraic fractions

CA4

- **Algebraic fractions** can be simplified by cancelling common factors in the numerator and denominator.

EXAMPLE

Simplify

a $\dfrac{4}{8x}$ **b** $\dfrac{5xy}{y^2}$ **c** $\dfrac{6p^2q^5}{3p^7q}$

> Remember that q means q^1.

a $\dfrac{1}{2x}$ cancelling by 4 **b** $\dfrac{5x}{y}$ cancelling by y **c** $\dfrac{2q^4}{p^5}$ cancelling by $3p^2q$

> When dividing powers of the same letter remember to subtract the powers.

If either the numerator or denominator is not in **factorised** form, factorise first and then remember to cancel factors.

EXAMPLE

Simplify

a $\dfrac{2x-6}{x^2-2x-3}$ **b** $\dfrac{4x^2-25}{2x^2+x-10}$

a $\dfrac{2x-6}{x^2-2x-3} = \dfrac{2(x-3)}{(x-3)(x+1)}$ factorise numerator and denominator

$= \dfrac{2}{(x+1)}$ cancel by $(x-3)$

b $\dfrac{4x^2-25}{2x^2+x-10} = \dfrac{(2x+5)(2x-5)}{(2x+5)(x-2)}$ factorise numerator and denominator

$= \dfrac{2x-5}{x-2}$ cancel by $(2x+5)$

You can cancel common factors in multiplication or division problems to make the calculation easier.

EXAMPLE

Simplify

a $\dfrac{p}{7} \div \dfrac{3p}{4}$ **b** $\dfrac{x^2-9}{7} \times \dfrac{5}{x-3}$

a $\dfrac{p}{7} \div \dfrac{3p}{4} = \dfrac{p}{7} \times \dfrac{4}{3p}$ reverse the quotient and change $\div$ to $\times$

$= \dfrac{4}{7 \times 3}$ cancel by p

$= \dfrac{4}{21}$

b $\dfrac{x^2-9}{7} \times \dfrac{5}{x-3} = \dfrac{(x+3)(x-3) \times 5}{7 \times (x-3)}$ factorise the quadratic term

$= \dfrac{5(x+3)}{7}$ cancel by $(x-3)$

114 **Algebraic fractions**

Exercise CA4

1 Simplify

a $\dfrac{10a}{5}$

b $\dfrac{6uv}{vw}$

c $\dfrac{7h}{h^4}$

d $\dfrac{4m^2}{2mn}$

e $\dfrac{6c^5d^3}{9d^8e^2}$

f $\dfrac{15r^6t^8}{20r^2t^{11}}$

g $\dfrac{24a^2b^4}{8a^3b^5}$

h $\dfrac{75(xy)^2}{25y}$

2 Simplify

a $\dfrac{x+2}{5(x+2)}$

b $\dfrac{4x-12}{7x-21}$

c $\dfrac{3x+6}{x^2+6x+8}$

d $\dfrac{x^2+9x+20}{3x+15}$

e $\dfrac{x^2-4x-32}{x^2-11x+24}$

f $\dfrac{x^2+x-12}{x^2-16}$

g $\dfrac{4x^2-9}{4x-6}$

h $\dfrac{2x^2+5x-3}{x^2-2x-15}$

i $\dfrac{4x^2+4x-15}{8x^2-10x-3}$

j $\dfrac{x^3+2x^2}{6x^3+13x^2+2x}$

3 A trapezium has area $(4x^2-3x-1)$ cm².
A triangle of area $(3x^2-5x+2)$ cm² is removed.
What fraction of the trapezium's area remains?
Give your answer in its simplest form.

4 By cancelling where possible, simplify these multiplication
and division calculations.

a $\dfrac{4p}{3} \times \dfrac{9}{4p}$

b $\dfrac{6ab}{7} \times \dfrac{2}{b}$

c $\dfrac{4m^2}{8} \times \dfrac{2n}{m^3}$

d $\dfrac{3}{g} \div \dfrac{g}{5}$

e $\dfrac{4w}{3} \div \dfrac{w}{2}$

f $\dfrac{2f^2}{p^3} \times \dfrac{p}{4f}$

g $\dfrac{y^2}{5} \div \dfrac{y^3}{25}$

h $\dfrac{x^2-11x+18}{12} \div \dfrac{x^2-17x+18}{24}$

5 A rectangle measures $\dfrac{x+2}{8}$ by $\dfrac{7}{x^2-4}$ and its area is $\dfrac{1}{4}$ m².

Set up an equation and solve it to find the dimensions
of this shape.

$\dfrac{x+2}{8}$

$\dfrac{7}{x^2-4}$

Quadratic equations

- **Quadratic equations** are of the form $ax^2 + bx + c = 0$. They typically have two solutions.

$a \neq 0$ but b or c could be 0.

You can solve a quadratic equation by **factorising**.

EXAMPLE

Solve using factors

a $x^2 - 4x - 60 = 0$

b $2x^2 - x - 15 = 0$

....

a $x^2 - 4x - 60 = 0$

$(x - 10)(x + 6) = 0$ factorising

$x = 10$ or -6 because either $(x - 10) = 0$
or $(x + 6) = 0$

b $2x^2 - x - 15 = 0$

$(2x + 5)(x - 3) = 0$ factorising

$x = -\dfrac{5}{2}$ or $x = 3$ because either $(2x + 5) = 0$
or $(x - 3) = 0$

You can solve a quadratic equation by **completing the square**.

The 2 values (10 and −6) are called the **roots** of the equation.

EXAMPLE

a Write $x^2 + 6x - 10$ in the form $(x + p^2) + q$ where p and q are integers.

b Hence solve $x^2 + 6x - 10 = 0$

....

a $(x + 3)^2 = x^2 + 6x + 9$, but you want $x^2 + 6x - 10$, so subtract -19

So $x^2 + 6x - 10 = (x + 3)^2 - 19$.

b Now $x^2 + 6x - 10 = 0$

$(x + 3)^2 - 19 = 0$ using our answer from **a**

$(x + 3)^2 = 19$ adding 19 to both sides

$x + 3 = \pm\sqrt{19}$ square rooting both sides

$x = -3 \pm \sqrt{19}$ subtracting 3 from both sides

Alternatively, you can solve a quadratic equation using **the quadratic formula**.

The roots here are left as **exact** values (in surd form).

EXAMPLE

Solve $2x^2 + x - 5 = 0$ giving your answer correct to 1 decimal place.

....

First note that $a = 2$, $b = 1$ and $c = -5$

Then use the quadratic formula $x = \dfrac{-b \pm \sqrt{b^2 - 4ac}}{2a}$

$$= \frac{-1 \pm \sqrt{1^2 - 4 \times 2 \times -5}}{2 \times 2}$$

$$= \frac{-1 \pm \sqrt{1 - -40}}{4}$$

$$= \frac{-1 \pm \sqrt{41}}{4}$$

$$= -1.9 \text{ or } 1.4 \text{ (to 1 dp)}$$

The accuracy demand (1 dp or 2 sf etc) is a big clue that you need to use the quadratic formula.

EXAMINER'S TIP

Even though Unit C is a calculator paper you may be asked for **exact** answers.

Exercise CA5

HIGH

1 Factorise and solve

a $x^2 + 7x + 12 = 0$ b $x^2 + 11x + 24 = 0$ c $x^2 - 5x - 14 = 0$ d $x^2 - x - 72 = 0$

e $x^2 + 3x - 28 = 0$ f $x^2 + 8x - 20 = 0$ g $x^2 - 10x + 24 = 0$ h $x^2 - 11x + 30 = 0$

i $x^2 - 8x = 0$ j $x^2 + 2x = 0$ k $x^2 - 16 = 0$ l $x^2 + 8x + 16 = 0$

2 Solve using factors

a $2x^2 + 5x + 2 = 0$ b $3x^2 - 7x - 6 = 0$ c $6x^2 + 5x + 1 = 0$ d $4x^2 + 19x - 5 = 0$

e $10x^2 + 11x - 6 = 0$ f $12x^2 - 25x + 12 = 0$ g $9x^2 - 1 = 0$ h $4x^2 + 12x + 9 = 0$

3   **i**   Write each expression in the form $(x + c)^2 + d$.

    ii   Write the minimum value of each of the expressions.

a $x^2 + 10x + 12$ b $x^2 + 4x + 7$ c $x^2 - 12x + 3$ d $x^2 - 2x + 11$

e $x^2 + 6x - 2$ f $x^2 + 20x - 16$ g $x^2 - 14x$ h $x^2 - 18x - 19$

4 Solve each equation by first writing it in the form $(x + p)^2 + q = 0$.
Leave your answers in exact form.

a $x^2 + 8x - 7 = 0$ b $x^2 + 6x + 2 = 0$ c $x^2 + 2x - 2 = 0$ d $x^2 + 12x + 7 = 0$

e $x^2 - 4x - 6 = 0$ f $x^2 - 6x - 1 = 0$ g $x^2 - 10x + 11 = 0$ h $x^2 - 16x + 62 = 0$

5 Use the quadratic formula to solve these equations.
Give the roots correct to 3 significant figures where appropriate.

a $x^2 - 5x - 5 = 0$ b $x^2 + 6x - 1 = 0$ c $2x^2 + 7x - 4 = 0$ d $2x^2 - 3x - 2 = 0$

e $3x^2 - 5x - 4 = 0$ f $4x^2 + 7x - 5 = 0$ g $5x^2 - 8x + 3 = 0$ h $6x + 7 - 2x^2 = 0$

6 The sides of this rectangle are given in centimetres. It has an area of $40\,\text{cm}^2$.

   a   Form and solve an equation in x.

   b   Hence show that the perimeter of the rectangle
is $28.5\,\text{cm}^2$ to 3 significant figures.

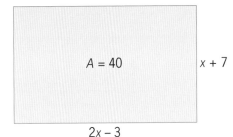

$A = 40$ $x + 7$

$2x - 3$

7 Copy and complete this solution.

$$2x^2 + 8x - 3 = 0$$
$$2[x^2 + \square x] - 3 = 0 \qquad \text{factorising first 2 terms}$$
$$2[(x + \square)^2 - \square] - 3 = 0 \qquad \text{completing the square}$$
$$2(x + \square)^2 - \square - 3 = 0 \qquad \text{expanding the square brackets}$$
$$2(x + \square)^2 - \square = 0 \qquad \text{simplifying}$$
$$2(x + \square)^2 = \square \qquad \text{adding to each side}$$
$$(x + \square)^2 = \square \qquad \text{dividing each side by 2}$$
$$x + \square = \pm\square \qquad \text{taking the square root of each side}$$
$$x = -\square \pm \square \qquad \text{subtracting from each side}$$
$$x = \square \text{ or } \square$$

UNIT C

Quadratic graphs

Graphs of quadratic functions have a distinctive **parabolic** shape.

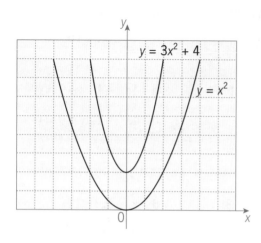

These graphs can be used to find approximate solutions to **quadratic equations**.

EXAMPLE

a Complete this table of values and draw the graph of $y = 2x^2 - 3$.

x	-2	-1.5	-1	-0.5	0	0.5	1	1.5	2
y	5	1.5		-2.5		-2.5		1.5	5

b Use your graph to solve $2x^2 - 3 = 0$.

c Use your graph to solve $2x^2 - 3 = -2$.

....

a When $x = -1$, $y = 2x^2 - 3$ When $x = 0$, $y = 2x^2 - 3$ When $x = 1$, $y = 2x^2 - 3$
$\qquad\qquad\qquad = 2 \times (-1)^2 - 3 \qquad\qquad\qquad = 2 \times (0)^2 - 3 \qquad\qquad\qquad = 2 \times 1^2 - 3$
$\qquad\qquad\qquad = 2 \times 1 - 3 \qquad\qquad\qquad\quad = 2 \times 0 - 3 \qquad\qquad\qquad\quad = 2 \times 1 - 3$
$\qquad\qquad\qquad = -1 \qquad\qquad\qquad\qquad\quad = -3 \qquad\qquad\qquad\qquad\quad = -1$

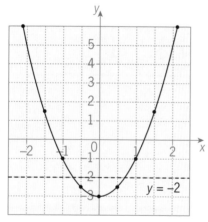

Quadratic graphs always look like ∪ or ∩.

b The solutions are where the graph crosses the line $y = 0$, that is, the x-axis.
Therefore the solutions are $x = -1.2$ and $x = 1.2$

c The solutions are where the line $y = 2x^2 - 3$ crosses the line $y = -2$.
Therefore the solutions are $x = -0.7$ and $x = 0.7$.

Exercise CA6

1 Draw the graphs of these functions for $-3 \leq x \leq 3$.

   a $y = x^2 - 2$
   b $y = x^2 + 3$
   c $y = x^2 - 5$
   d $y = 2x^2 - 1$

   e $y = 2x^2 - 3$
   f $y = 3x^2 - 7$
   g $y = 10 - x^2$
   h $y = 2 - x^2$

2 Use your graphs from question 1 to write down approximate
solutions to the following equations.

   a $x^2 - 2 = 0$
   b $x^2 + 3 = 8$
   c $x^2 - 5 = 5$
   d $2x^2 - 1 = 0$

   e $2x^2 - 3 = 15$
   f $3x^2 - 7 = -2$
   g $10 - x^2 = 6$
   h $2 - x^2 = -3$

3 Solve these equations using the graphs (one of the equations has no solutions).

   a $4x^2 - 6 = 0$
   b $3x^2 + 3 = 8$
   c $8 - x^2 = 2$

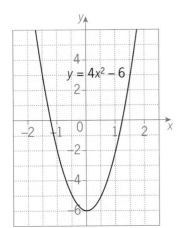 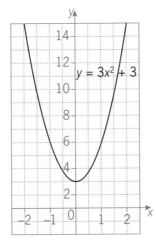 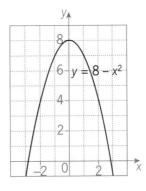

   d $4x^2 - 6 = 2$
   e $3x^2 + 3 = 3$
   f $8 - x^2 = 9$

4 Look at the graph of $y = 4x^2 - 6$ in question **3a**.
The equation $4x^2 - 6 = k$ has no solutions. What can you say about k?

5 Draw the graphs of these functions for $-3 \leq x \leq 3$.

   a $y = x^2 - 2x - 3$
   b $y = x^2 - x - 4$
   c $y = x^2 - 4x + 7$

   d $y = 2x^2 - 3x + 5$
   e $y = 3x^2 + x - 1$
   f $y = 7 + 6x - 2x^2$

6 Use your graphs from question 5 to write down approximate
solutions to these equations.

   a $x^2 - 2x - 3 = 2$
   b $x^2 + x - 4 = 0$
   c $x^2 - 4x + 7 = 5$

   d $2x^2 - 3x + 5 = 10$
   e $3x^2 + x - 1 = 5$
   f $7 + 6x - 2x^2 = 9$

7 A rectangular piece of card of sides $3x - 2$ cm
and $2x + 3$ cm has squares of side x removed from
each corner as shown to make a net of an open box.

   a Find an expression for the volume, V cm³, of the box
       in terms of x.

   b Draw the graph of V against x for $0 \leq x \leq 4$.

   c Explain why $x > 2$.

   d Find x such that the volume of the open box is 20 cm³.

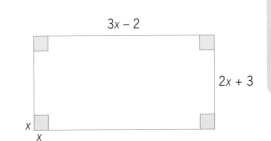

Simultaneous linear and quadratic equations (CA7)

- You can use **substitution** to solve simultaneous equations where one is a quadratic and the other is linear.

EXAMPLE

Solve $y = x^2 + 4$

$y - x = 6$

> If possible, try to avoid **fractions** in the equation you are substituting.

$y - x = 6$ so $y = x + 6$

Substitute $y = x + 6$ into the quadratic equation:

$y = x^2 + 4$

$x + 6 = x^2 + 4$ Substituting $x + 6$ for y

$x^2 - x - 2 = 0$ Make the equation $= 0$

$(x - 2)(x + 1) = 0$ Factorise

$x = 2$ or -1

> You could have substituted for x rather than y. You would get the same answers but it would have involved a bit more work. Try it and see.

> If the quadratic does not factorise you would solve it using the quadratic formula.

Now substitute x back into the linear equation to find the y values.

When x is 2, $y = x + 6$ When x is -1, $y = x + 6$

$y = 2 + 6$ $y = -1 + 6$

$= 8$ $= 5$

Therefore the solutions are $x = -1$, $y = 5$ and $x = 2$, $y = 8$.

> Don't forget to give pairs of solutions for both x and y. Be clear which x goes with which y.

- Solving simultaneous equations is equivalent to finding the intersection points of their graphs.

EXAMPLE

The diagram shows the graphs of $y = x^2 - 5x + 4$ and $2x + 3y = 6$.

Use the graphs to solve the simultaneous equations

$y = x^2 - 5x + 4$

$2x + 3y = 6$

giving your solutions correct to 1 decimal place.

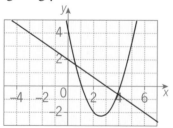

EXAMINER'S TIP:

These questions can ask you to use the crossing points to find solutions (as this question has done) or you may have to solve the equations to find the crossing points.

If you are asked to find the points, make sure you give your answer as coordinates using brackets.

The points of intersection are at (0.5, 1.7) and (3.8, −0.5) therefore the approximate solutions are $x = 0.5$, $y = 1.7$

Exercise CA7

HIGH

1 Solve these simultaneous equations using substitution.

   a $y = x^2 - 5$
      b $y = x^2 + 2x$
      c $y = x - x^2$

      $y = x + 1$
          $y = x + 2$
          $y = x - 4$

   d $y = x^2 + x - 5$
   e $y = 2x^2 - 3x$
   f $y = x^2 + x + 1$

      $y + x = 19$
         $y + 2x = 6$
        $3y - x = 8$

2 Solve these simultaneous equations, giving your solutions
correct to 1 decimal place. One of these gives no solutions – which one is it?

   a $y + x^2 + 3x = 1$
   b $y^2 + x + 1 = 0$
   c $y^2 - 2x + 3 = 0$

      $y + x + 1 = 0$
       $y - 8 - x = 0$
      $y + 2x - 8 = 0$

   d $y^2 = 3x - 2$
      e $y^2 + y + x = 0$
   f $2y = 3x^2 - 2x + 4$

      $y + 3x - 3 = 0$
      $y = 2x - 4$
        $3y - 4x = 8$

3 The graphs of $y = 2x^2 + x - 3$, $y = 2x - 1$ and $6x + 7y = 50$ are shown.

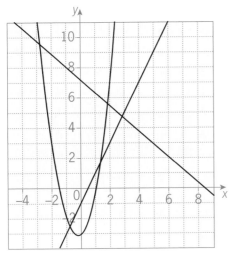

Use the graphs to solve the following pairs of
simultaneous equations, giving your solutions correct
to 1 decimal place.

   a $y = 2x^2 + x - 3$
   b $y = 2x^2 + x - 3$
   c $y = 2x - 1$

      $y = 2x - 1$
        $6x + 7y = 50$
      $6x + 7y = 50$

4 The diagram shows a sketch of the graphs of
$y^2 + 3x = 2 + y$ and $y + 2x + 7 = 0$.

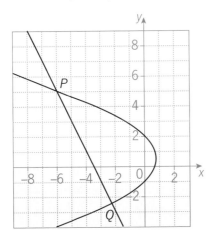

Use algebra to find the coordinates of P and Q and hence find the distance PQ.

Real-life graphs

- You need to be able to generate, construct, interpret and discuss graphs from real life. These could include:
  - ➤ graphs made from straight-line segments
  - ➤ quadratic graphs
  - ➤ other functions

EXAMPLE

This sketch graph shows how much Jayne pays for her gas depending on what volume she uses.
Describe what the different sections of the graph represent.

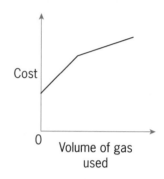

Because the graph doesn't start at the origin, there is a fixed standing charge.
The first straight line section represents a fixed charge per unit volume.
The second section has a smaller gradient, so it represents a **lower** fixed charge per unit volume.

EXAMPLE

When a car driver brakes, the *stopping distance* of the car (*s* metres) is the sum of the *thinking distance* (*t* metres) and the *braking distance* (*b* metres).
These distances are related to the car's speed (*v* m/s) as follows: $t = \dfrac{3v}{10}$ and $b = \dfrac{3v^2}{200}$.
Plot the graph of *s* against *v* for $0 \le v \le 50$ and use it to find the speed that gives a stopping distance of 30 m.

The equation needed is $s = \dfrac{3v}{10} + \dfrac{3v^2}{200}$ giving this table of values:

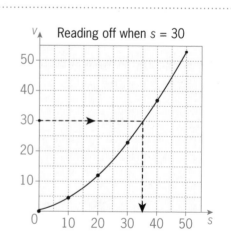

v	0	10	20	30	40	50
s	0	4.5	12	22.5	36	52.5

When *s* = 30 the speed is approximately 35 m/s.

Exercise CA8

1 The graph shows Adam's journey from home to his swimming lesson. He walks to the bus stop and then gets the bus to the swimming pool.
At the pool he waits for 10 minutes and then has a 45-minute lesson.
His mother picks him up from the pool and drives him home in her car, a journey that takes 10 minutes.
   a Copy and complete the distance–time graph.
   b Calculate the average speed for each of the three parts of Adam's journey: walking, bus and car.
   c What feature **of the graph** shows that the bus journey is faster than the walking section?
   d Describe two ways in which this graph is not an accurate representation of what happens in real life.

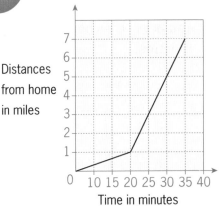

2 A ball is thrown into the air.
The formula $y = 20x - 4x^2$ shows its height y metres above the ground x seconds after it is thrown.
   a Complete a table of values for x and y to show the height of the ball during its first five seconds.
   b Use your table to plot a graph to show the ball's height against time.
   c Use your graph to find
      i   the maximum height reached by the ball and the time at which it reaches this height
      ii   two times when the ball is 12 metres above the ground
      iii the interval of time when the ball is above 15 metres.

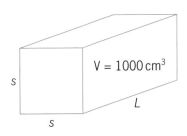

3 A block of steel of volume 1000 cm³ is to be melted down and made into a cuboid with a square cross-section.
   a Calculate the length, L, of the cuboid when the cross-section has side, s, of 5 cm.
   b Write down the formula for L in terms of s.
   c Draw the graph of L for $5 \leq s \leq 30$.

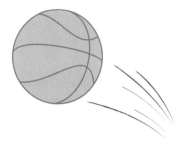

V = 1000 cm³

s

s

L

- You need to recognise the graphs of these **non-linear** functions:

$y = x^3$ is called a **cubic** function, $y = \dfrac{1}{x}$ is the **reciprocal** function and $y = 2^x$ is an **exponential** function.

$y = x^3$

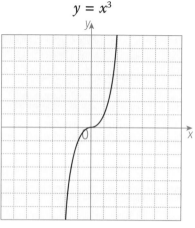

This is a **cubic** function

$y = \dfrac{1}{x}$

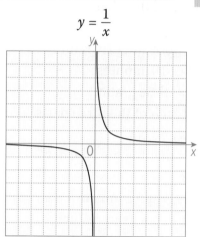

This is a **reciprocal** function

$y = 2^x, y = 3^x$ etc

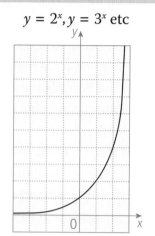

This is an **exponential** function

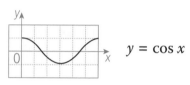 $y = \cos x$

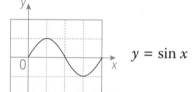 $y = \sin x$

These are **trigonometric** functions

You can draw graphs of these functions by working out points.

EXAMPLE

a Complete this table of values and draw the graph of $y = x^3 + x^2 - 2x - 1$.

x	-2	-1.5	-1	-0.5	0	0.5	1	1.5
y	-1	0.875		0.125	-1		-1	1.625

b Use your graph to solve $x^3 + x^2 - 2x - 1 = 0.5$.

....

a When $x = -1$,
$y = x^3 + x^2 - 2x - 1$
$y = (-1)^3 + (-1)^2 - (2 \times -1) - 1$
$= -1 + 1 + 2 - 1$
$= 1$

When $x = 0.5$,
$y = x^3 + x^2 - 2x - 1$
$y = 0.5^3 + 0.5^2 - 2 \times 0.5 - 1$
$= 0.125 + 0.25 - 1 - 1$
$= -1.625$

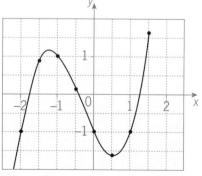

Draw your graph freehand and make the 'turning points' curved not angular.

b The solutions are where the graph crosses the line $y = 0.5$.
Therefore the solutions are $x = -1.7$, $x = -0.7$ and $x = 1.3$.

Exercise CA9

1 Draw sketches of the following graphs.

   a $y = \cos x$ **b** $y = \frac{1}{x}$ **c** $y = 5^x$ **d** $y = \sin x$ **e** $y = x^3$

2 Draw the following graphs using the given values of x.

   a $y = x^3 - 2x^2 - x$

x	−1	−0.5	0	0.5	1	1.5	2	2.5	3
y									

   b $y = \dfrac{6}{x - 2}$

x	−4	−3	−2	−1	0	1	3	4	5	6
y										

   c $y = 2^x$

x	−2	−1	0	1	3	4
y						

   d $y = 2 \sin x + 1$

x	0	30	60	90	120	150	180
y							

3 **a** Draw the graphs of $y = \dfrac{4}{x + 2}$ and $y = x - 1$ on the same axes for $-4 \le x \le 4$.

   b There is one value of x for which you cannot calculate the y-value for $y = \dfrac{4}{x + 2}$. State which value. Explain why it cannot be calculated.

   c Use your graphs to solve these simultaneous equations.

$$y = \frac{4}{x + 2}$$

$$y = x - 1$$

   d Explain **why** the solutions of the simultaneous equations have the same x-values as the solution of $x^2 + x - 6 = 0$.

4 Match each graph with the appropriate real-life situation described below.

   a The mass, M g, of a cubical steel block and the length of its side, l cm.

   b The time, T hours, to drive 60 miles at an average speed of s mph is given by $\dfrac{60}{s}$.

   c The population, P, of the UK n years after 1800 can be given approximately as $P = 9 \times 1.01^n$.

   d The depth, d, of a river h hours after high tide is given by the equation $d = 4 \cos 30h + 7$.

Sketch each graph and label the axes with the appropriate letter.

a

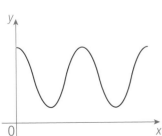

b

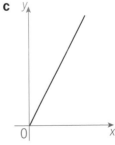

c

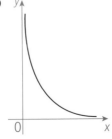

d

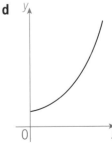

- Given the graph of $y = f(x)$ you need to know these transformations:

  $y = f(x) + a$ is a translation of $y = f(x)$ by the vector $\begin{pmatrix} 0 \\ a \end{pmatrix}$

  $y = f(x + a)$ is a translation of $y = f(x)$ by the vector $\begin{pmatrix} -a \\ 0 \end{pmatrix}$

  $y = af(x)$ is a stretch of $y = f(x)$, factor a, in the y direction

  $y = f(ax)$ is a stretch of $y = f(x)$, factor $\frac{1}{a}$, in the x direction

EXAMPLE

The diagram shows a sketch of the graph of $y = f(x)$.
Draw sketches of

a $y = f(x) + 2$ **b** $y = f(4x)$

showing clearly the coordinates of each end of the graph.

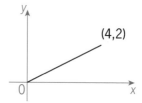

a $y = f(x) + 2$ is a translation by $\begin{pmatrix} 0 \\ 2 \end{pmatrix}$.   **b** $y = f(4x)$ is a stretch, factor $\frac{1}{4}$, in the x direction.

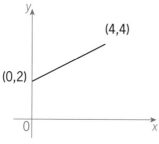

The y values have all been increased by 2.

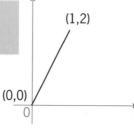

The x values have all been multiplied by $\frac{1}{4}$

EXAMPLE

Write down a possible equation for each graph.

a

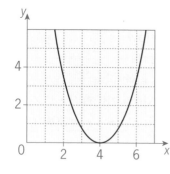

b

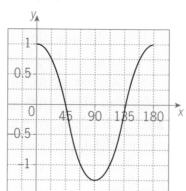

You can tell that $y = \cos x$ has been stretched by $\frac{1}{2}$ because its period is 180, half of the usual 360.

a This graph is a translation of $y = x^2$ by the vector $\begin{pmatrix} 4 \\ 0 \end{pmatrix}$, therefore the equation is $y = (x - 4)^2$.

Using $y = f(x + a)$ with $a = -4$.

b This graph is a stretch of $y = \cos x$, factor $\frac{1}{2}$, in the x direction, therefore the equation is $y = \cos 2x$.

Using $y = f(ax)$ with $a = \frac{1}{2}$.

Exercise CA10

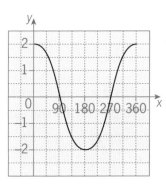

HIGH

1 Suggest possible equations for these graphs.

a

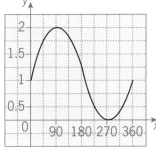

b

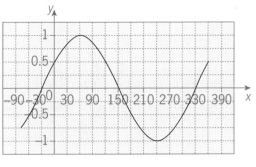

c

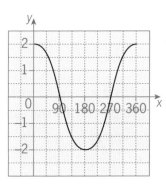

d

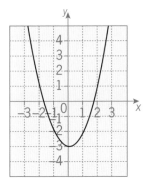

e

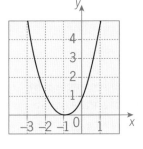

f

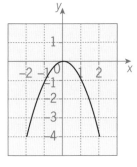

2 Here is a sketch of the graph of $y = f(x)$.
   A is the point $(6, 4)$.

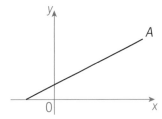

Find the image of point A under
these transformations.

a $y = f(x) + 4$ **b** $y = 5f(x)$ **c** $y = f(x - 7)$

d $y = -f(x)$ **e** $y = f(x + 5)$ **f** $y = \frac{1}{2}f(x)$

g $y = f(x) - 1$ **h** $y = f(3x)$ **i** $y = f(-x)$

> $y = -f(x)$ is the same as a reflection in
> the x-axis.
>
> $y = f(-x)$ is the same as a reflection
> in the y-axis.

3 For each of these equations, draw a new set of axes, sketch the
   graph of $y = x^2$ and then sketch the required graph on the same axes.
   a $y = (x + 6)^2$ **b** $y = 4x^2$ **c** $y = x^2 - 4$

4 Given that the graphs of $y = \sin(x + 60)$ and $y = \cos(x - t)$ are identical,
   find a possible value of t.

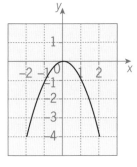

UNIT C

Area and perimeter of compound shapes
CG1

The perimeter of a shape is the total distance around its edge. It is measured in terms of centimetres, metres, inches and so on.

LOOK BACK
See topic AG1 on page 26 to revise the metric and imperial systems.

- The area is a measure of the amount of space enclosed by the shape and is measured in terms of a standard unit such as cm² or m² (the unit is always squared).

Rectangle

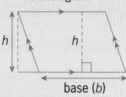
Parallelogram

Triangle

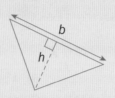

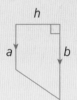
Trapezium

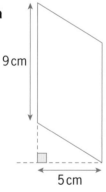

Area of rectangle = lw
Area of parallelogram = bh
Area of triangle = $\frac{1}{2}bh$
Area of trapezium = $\frac{1}{2}(a + b)h$

EXAMPLE

Find the area of the following shapes (all units are cm).

a

9 cm

5 cm

b

11 cm

10 cm

2 cm

c

5   12

13

a Parallelogram area

$= 5 \times 9 = 45\,\text{cm}^2$

b Trapezium area

$= \frac{1}{2} \times (11 + 2) \times 10 = 65\,\text{cm}^2$

c Triangle area

$= \frac{1}{2} \times 5 \times 12 = 30\,\text{cm}^2$

The area of a compound shape can be calculated by dividing the shape into simple component areas first and then summing or subtracting as appropriate to get the overall area.

EXAMPLE

Find the area of this logo for a haulage company.

Logo = trapezium + triangle

$= \frac{1}{2} \times (9 + 3) \times 7 + \frac{1}{2} \times 9 \times 4 = 42 + 18 = 60\,\text{m}^2$

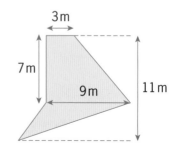
3 m

7 m

9 m   11 m

128   **Area and perimeter of compound shapes**

A modern art painting is hung in the school reception area. It is coloured white and orange as shown.
Find the area of orange paint.

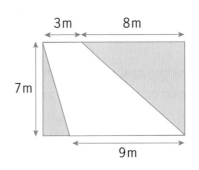

Area = area of rectangle − area of trapezium

$$= 7 \times 11 - \frac{1}{2} \times (3 + 9) \times 7 = 35\,\text{m}^2$$

Exercise CG1

MEDIUM

1 Find the area of these shapes.

a

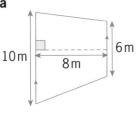

b

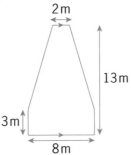

c

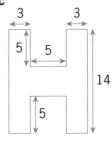

d

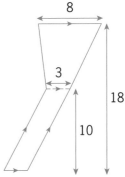

2 Find the value of x and hence the area of this trapezium.

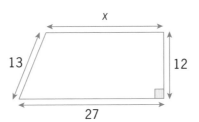

> You can use Pythagoras' theorem to help you with this question.

3 A path is shown shaded in the diagram.
The path encloses a lawn.

  a Find the area of the lawn.

  b Over the years the path has become worn down
so the owner decides to replace the paving slabs. A slab of $1\,\text{m}^2$
cost £8. How much will the owner need to spend to redo his path?

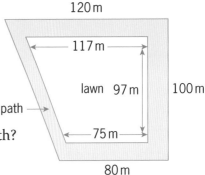

4 Draw sketches of three trapeziums which have an area of $60\,\text{m}^2$.

5 Using this diagram as a guide give a clearly-reasoned justification
for the formula for the area of a trapezium as $\frac{1}{2}(a + b)h$.

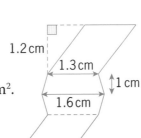

6 The design for a badge is proposed,
made of two congruent parallelograms
and two congruent trapeziums.
It is to be covered in gold leaf which costs £16 per cm^2.
Find the cost of covering the front of the badge.

Circumference and area of a circle (CG2)

If you know the radius or diameter you can use π (pronounced 'pi')
to find the circumference and area of a circle.

- Circumference (perimeter) of
  circle $C = \pi \times d = \pi d = 2\pi r$
  Area of circle $A = \pi \times r^2 = \pi r^2$

  Circumference is a length so is
  measured in cm, m, inches, ...
  Area is measured in cm², m², ...

You can use your calculator value for π,
though it is approximately 3.142 or $\frac{22}{7}$.
π is a non-terminating and non-recurring
decimal.

EXAMPLE

Find the circumference and area of a circle of radius
6 cm, leaving your answer in exact form. (No calculator
is needed for this problem!)

Note that units don't have to be put in until
the final answer.

$C = 2\pi r = 2 \times \pi \times 6 = 12\pi\,\text{cm}$ $A = \pi r^2 = \pi \times 6^2 = 36\pi\,\text{cm}^2$

- You should know about sectors, arc length, chords and segments.

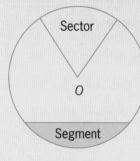

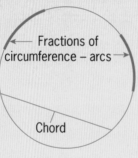

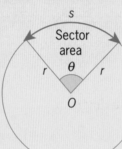

Arc length, $s = \dfrac{\theta}{360} \times 2\pi r$

Sector area $= \dfrac{\theta}{360} \times \pi r^2$

EXAMPLE

Find the area and total perimeter of the sector OAB.

Sector area $= \dfrac{40}{360} \times \pi \times 12^2 = 50.265... = 50.3\,\text{m}^2$ (3 sf)

Arc length $= \dfrac{40}{360} \times 2 \times \pi \times 12 = 8.377... = 8.38\,\text{m}$ (3 sf)

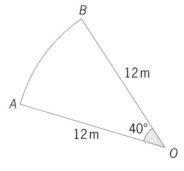

EXAMPLE

The area of a sector with radius 4.2 m is 34 m².
Find the angle θ subtended by that sector.

This will be in Ans memory on calculator.
Try not to round until the final answer.

$\dfrac{\theta}{360} \times \pi \times 4.2^2 = 34$ so $\dfrac{\theta}{360} = 34 \div (\pi \times 4.2^2) = 0.61352...$
and hence $\theta = 0.61352... \times 360 = 221°$

Find the area of the segment *ATB*.

Area of segment = area of sector − area of triangle

$= \dfrac{60}{360} \times \pi \times 5^2 - \dfrac{1}{2} \times 5 \times 5 \times \sin 60 = 2.26\,\text{cm}^2$

Using area of triangle formula $\frac{1}{2}$ ab sin C

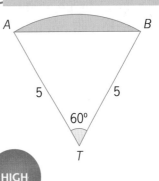

Exercise CG2

HIGH

1 Find the area and circumference of a circle of diameter 12 m, giving your answers
   a in exact form   **b** to 3 sf.

2 The diameter of each wheel of Mike's bicycle is 80 cm.
   a Find the circumference of a wheel.
   b If the wheel turns 200 times, how far has the wheel travelled (in metres)?
   c How many times does the wheel turn if Mike cycles 10 km?

3 A garden at the Chelsea Flower Show is in the shape of three
   semi-circles attached to the sides of an equilateral triangle.
   a If the equilateral triangle has side of length 20 m,
        find the perimeter of the garden.
   b Find the total area of the garden.

4 For the sector shown calculate
   a the arc length *AB*
   b the sector area
   c the total perimeter of the sector.

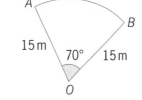

5 The *exact* area of a sector of radius 10 m is $40\,\pi\,\text{cm}^2$.
   Find the angle subtended by the sector.

6 Find the area of the shaded segment shown.

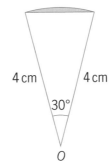

7 A badge is designed as shown.
   Calculate the area of the shaded region.

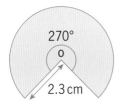

8 Three circular tubes are held together by a band of rubber.
   Each tube has diameter 2 metres.
   What is the stretched length of the band?

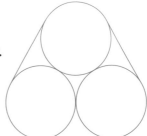

Surface area and volume CG3

- A **prism** is a special type of object which has the same cross-section throughout its length.
  The volume of a prism = area of cross-section × length of prism.

> A simple example would be a cube of side 4 cm.
>
> A cube has six faces, each with an area of 16 cm² hence the surface area is 6 × 16 = 96 cm².

Commonly encountered prisms are cuboids, triangular prisms and cylinders.
The surface area of a prism is the sum of the areas of all the faces of the prism.

EXAMPLE

Find the surface area of prism A and the volume of prisms A and B.

Prism A

Cross-section is a triangle: area $\frac{1}{2} \times 8 \times 6 = 24\,\text{m}^2$

Surface area = 2 tri + 3 rectangle

$$= 2 \times 24 + (10 \times 9) + (9 \times 6) + (8 \times 9)$$
$$= 48 + 216 = 264\,\text{m}^2$$

Volume = 24 × 9 = 216 m³

Prism B

Volume of prism = area of trapezium × length

$$= \frac{1}{2} \times (3 + 8) \times 4 \times 7 = 154\,\text{m}^3$$

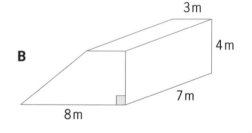
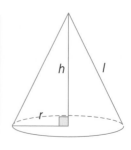

- A prism of particular importance is the cylinder.
  Volume = $\pi r^2 h$ curved surface area = $2\pi rh$
  surface area of closed cylinder = $2\pi rh + 2\pi r^2$

EXAMPLE

Find the curved surface area of this barrel.
What is the capacity of the barrel in litres?

Curved surface area = $2\pi rh = 2\pi \times 0.8 \times 2$
$$= 10.1\,\text{m}^2$$

Volume = $\pi r^2 h = \pi \times 0.8^2 \times 2 = 4.02\,\text{m}^3$
$$= 4.02 \times 1000\,\text{cm}^2 = 4020\,\text{litres}$$

Not all solid shapes are prisms and some objects have their own special formulae for volume and surface area.

- Sphere: volume $= \frac{4}{3}\pi r^3$ surface area = $4\pi r^2$

  Cone: volume = $\frac{1}{3}\pi r^2 h$ curved surface area = $\pi r l$

  total surface area = $\pi r l + \pi r^2$

  Pyramid: volume = $\frac{1}{3}$ base area × perpendicular height

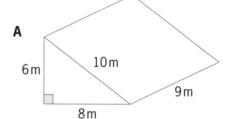

> l is slant height
> h is vertical height of cone

The shaded sector is folded to make a cone.
Find the base radius of the cone formed and find the
volume of the cone, leaving your answer in terms of π.

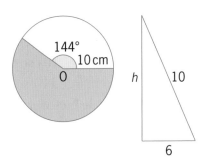

The arc length of the sector becomes the circumference
of the base of the cone.

Arc length $= \dfrac{216}{360} \times 2 \times \pi \times 10 = 12\pi$

Let R be the base radius of cone, then $2\pi R = 12\pi$ so
$R = 6\,\text{cm}$

Volume of cone $= \dfrac{1}{3} \times \pi \times 6^2 \times$ height of cone

$\qquad\qquad\qquad = \dfrac{1}{3} \times \pi \times 6^2 \times 8 = 96\pi$ ◄────── $h = \sqrt{(10^2 - 6^2)} = \sqrt{64} = 8$

Exercise CG3

HIGH

1 **a** Find the volumes of the following prisms.

i 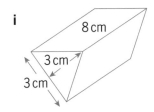 **ii** 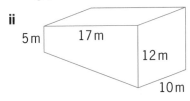 **iii**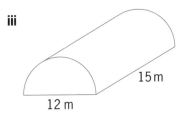

b Find the surface area of the semicircular prism in part **iii**.

2 Find the volume and curved surface area of the following closed objects.

a 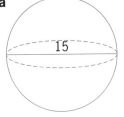 **b**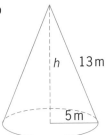

3 A sphere has a volume of $95\,\text{cm}^3$. Find its surface area.

4 A metal ball-bearing is dropped into a cylindrical flask
and it sinks to the bottom. The ball is completely covered
by water. Find how much the water level rises in the flask.

5 A sphere fits perfectly inside a cylinder. Find the ratio of the
volume of the sphere to the volume of the cylinder.

Length, area and volume scale factors $\boxed{\text{CG4}}$

- If an enlargement has scale factor p then the perimeter scale factor is p and the area scale factor is p^2.
- If a solid shape is enlarged by scale factor p, the lengths all increase by a scale factor p, the surface area of the shape increases by scale factor p^2 and the volume increases by scale factor p^3.

EXAMPLE

A cuboid is enlarged with scale factor 3. Using scale factors calculate the surface area and volume of the enlarged cuboid if the original cuboid has surface area $416\,\text{cm}^2$ and volume $480\,\text{cm}^3$.

Area scale factor = 3^2 = 9 so surface area of enlarged cuboid is $9 \times 416 = 3744\,\text{cm}^2$
Volume scale factor = 3^3 = 27 so volume of enlarged cuboid is $27 \times 480 = 12\,960\,\text{cm}^3$

Unit conversions:
$1\,\text{cm} = 10\,\text{mm}$ $\qquad$ $1\,\text{m} = 100\,\text{cm}$
$1\,\text{cm}^2 = 10^2\,\text{mm}^2 = 100\,\text{mm}^2$
$1\,\text{m}^2 = 100^2\,\text{cm}^2 = 10\,000\,\text{cm}^2$
$1\,\text{cm}^3 = 10^3\,\text{mm}^3 = 1000\,\text{mm}^3$
$1\,\text{m}^3 = 100^3\,\text{cm}^3 = 1\,000\,000\,\text{cm}^3$

EXAMPLE

Two mathematically similar tubs of double cream are shown.
Find the diameter of the circular lid of the smaller tub.

Volume scale factor $= \dfrac{300}{400} = 0.75$

so length factor $= \sqrt[3]{0.75}$

diameter, $d = \sqrt[3]{0.75} \times 10 = 9.1\,\text{cm}$ (1 dp)

EXAMPLE

Two spheres, one of radius $3\,\text{cm}$ and the other of radius $12\,\text{cm}$, are dipped in silver paint. How much more silver paint is required for the larger sphere?

Length factor = $12 \div 3 = 4$ so area factor = 4^2 = 16 and 16 times as much paint is required.

EXAMPLE

A chocolate bar manufacturer decides to produce a new, larger bar in which the sides of the original bar are all increased by 16%.
The original bar cost £1.24. What would be a fair price to charge for the new bar?

The length factor would be 1.16 so the volume factor would be $1.16^3 = 1.560896$.
The new price would be $1.24 \times 1.16^3 = 1.9355$, therefore a fair price would be about £1.94.

Exercise CG4

1 Box A has been enlarged to box B.

   a What is the scale factor of enlargement?

   b What is the scale factor for area?

   c If the area of the top of box A is 12 cm²
what is the area of the top of box B?

   d What is the scale factor for volume?

   e If the volume of box B is 342 cm³ what is the volume
of box A?

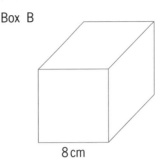

Box A   2 cm

Box B   8 cm

2 Mike has two identical shaped vases. One is 18 cm tall, the
other 9 cm tall. The smaller vase can hold 0.7 litres of water.
How much can the larger vase contain?

3 The pattern for a panel of a size 8 dress requires 300 cm²
of cloth. The width of the pattern is 12 cm. The width of an
identical pattern for a size 14 dress is 16 cm. Find the area of
cloth required for the same panel in a size 14 dress.

4 **a** Calculate the area of this symmetrical shape.

   b If the lengths of this shape are increased by scale factor 4,
calculate the area of the enlarged shape.

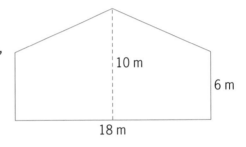

10 m

6 m

18 m

5 Convert the following units to the units given in brackets.

   a 4 cm² (mm²)   **b** 9 cm³ (mm³)   **c** 12 000 mm² (cm²)   **d** 5 km² (m²)

   e 7.3 m² (cm²)   **f** 3 200 000 cm³ (m³)   **g** 435 000 000 m² (km²)

6 Two cylinders, A and B, are mathematically similar.
The surface area of A is 2000 cm² and of B 125 cm².
If the volume of A is 3400 cm³, calculate the volume of cylinder B.

7 A model aeroplane is $\frac{1}{20}$ the length of the real plane.

   The area of both of the wings on the real plane is 800 m².
Find the total wing area on the model, giving
your final answer in cm².

Sine and cosine rules

The **sine and cosine rules** allow you to work out lengths and angles in triangles that are not right-angled.

Sine rule:

$$\frac{a}{\sin A} = \frac{b}{\sin B} = \frac{c}{\sin C} \quad \text{or} \quad \frac{\sin A}{a} = \frac{\sin B}{b} = \frac{\sin C}{c}$$

Cosine rule:

$$a^2 = b^2 + c^2 - 2bc\cos A \text{ or } \cos A = \frac{b^2 + c^2 - a^2}{2bc}$$

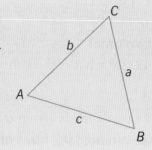

These rules are supplied on the examination board formulae sheet though it is recommended you learn them as well.

EXAMPLE

Find the unknown side and angle in these triangles.

a Find BC.

b Find angle Q.

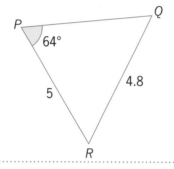

a $\dfrac{BC}{\sin 28°} = \dfrac{5}{\sin 27°} \Rightarrow BC = \dfrac{5\sin 28°}{\sin 27°} = 5.17\,\text{cm}\,(3\,\text{sf})$

b $\dfrac{\sin 64}{4.8} = \dfrac{\sin Q}{5}$

$\sin Q = \dfrac{5\sin 64}{4.8}$

$Q = \sin^{-1} 0.936\ldots$

$Q = 69.4°$

EXAMPLE

Find the unknown side and angle in these triangles.

a Find PR.

b Find angle Y.

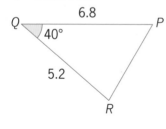

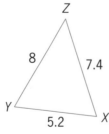

$PR^2 = 5.2^2 + 6.8^2 - 2 \times 5.2 \times 6.8 \cos 40° = 19.105\ldots$

$PR = \sqrt{19.105\ldots} = 4.37\,\text{cm}\,(3\,\text{sf})$

- Area of a triangle = $\frac{1}{2}\,ab\sin C = \frac{1}{2}\,ac\sin B = \frac{1}{2}\,bc\sin A$

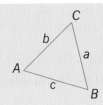

Find the area of these triangles.

a

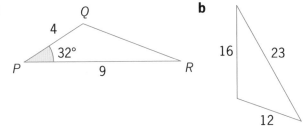

b

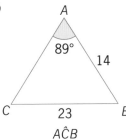

a Area$= \frac{1}{2} \times 4 \times 9 \times \sin 32° = 9.54\,\text{cm}^2$

b First you need to calculate
an angle, for example A.

$\cos A = \dfrac{(16^2 + 12^2 - 23^2)}{(2 \times 16 \times 12)} = -0.3359\ldots$

$A = \cos^{-1}(-0.3359\ldots) = 109.6°$

Then you can use the formula to find the
area:

Area $= \dfrac{1}{2} \times 16 \times 12 \times \sin 109.6° = 90.4\,\text{cm}^2$

Exercise CG5

HIGH

1 Find the missing sides and angles as indicated in these triangles.

a

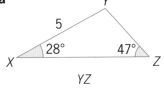

b

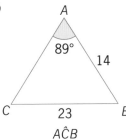

c

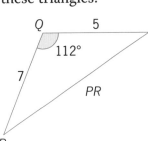

d

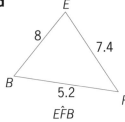

2 X and Y are two points on a jetty and B is a buoy. Frank measures
the distance XY as 40 m and the angles BXY and BYX as
47.5° and 54° respectively. Find the length BX.

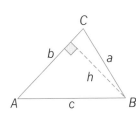

3 Two ships leave Dingle at the same time. One of them travels NW
at an average speed of 10.5 km/h while the other travels at 14 km/h
on a bearing of 280°. How far apart are they after two hours?

4 Two adjacent sides of a parallelogram are 8 cm and 7.5 cm.
If the shorter diagonal is 9 cm find the length of the other diagonal.

5 By using this triangle prove that the area of the triangle is $\frac{1}{2}\,ab \sin C$.
Hence find the area of an equilateral triangle of side 7 m.

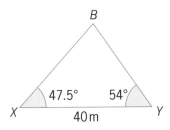

6 Given that the area of this isosceles triangle
is 25 m², find the size of angle x.

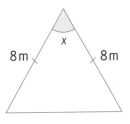

In 3D problems the approach is to extract a relevant 2D triangle and use that to find the missing side or length.

← **LOOK BACK**

See topic AG5 on page 34 to revise Pythagoras' theorem in 3D.

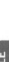

EXAMPLE

a Find QU
b Find WU
c Find angle QWU

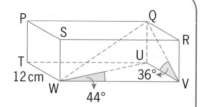

a $\tan 36 = \dfrac{QU}{12} \therefore QU = 12 \tan 36 = 8.72\,\text{cm (3sf)}$

b $\sin 44 = \dfrac{12}{WU} \therefore WU = \dfrac{12}{\sin 44} = 17.3\,\text{cm (3sf)}$

c $\tan W = \dfrac{8.7}{17.3} = 0.502\ldots$

$W = \tan^{-1} 0.502\ldots = 26.7° \,(3\,\text{sf})$

EXAMPLE

In the rectangular-based pyramid the vertex X is 6 m above the centre of the base rectangle.

a Find the length XB.
b Find the angle between XB and the base ABCD.
c Find the total surface area of the pyramid.

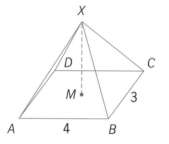

a Consider the triangle XMB

$MB^2 = 3^2 + 2^2 = 13$

$MB = \sqrt{13}$

$XB^2 = MB^2 + XM^2 = 13 + 36 = 49$

$XB = \sqrt{49} = 7$

b Required angle is $XBM = \tan^{-1}\dfrac{6}{\sqrt{13}} = 59.0°$

c To find the total surface area we need to find the area of the faces of the triangles and add them to the rectangular base area.

So consider triangle XAB:

Height of triangle $= \sqrt{(7^2 - 2^2)} = \sqrt{45}$

$\therefore$ area $= \dfrac{1}{2} \times 4 \times \sqrt{45} = 2\sqrt{45}$ similarly

triangle $XBC = \dfrac{1}{2} \times 3 \times \sqrt{46.75}$

Hence total area $= 2 \times 2\sqrt{45} + 2 \times \dfrac{1}{2} \times 3 \times \sqrt{46.75} + 4 \times 3 = 59.3\,\text{cm}^2$

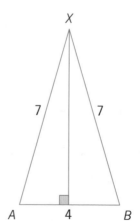

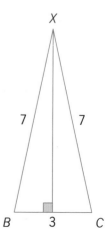

Exercise CG6

1 a Find the length DB.
   b Find the length DZ.
   c Find the angle BDZ.

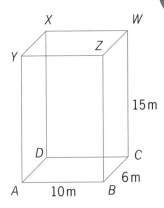

2 The height of this pyramid is 6.4 m.
   a Find the length of PR.
   b Find the size of the angle TRP.

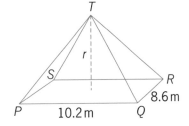

3 A cube PQRSTUVW is of side 10 cm.
   a Find RU.
   b Find SU.
   c Find the angle between SU and
      the base of the cube TUVW.

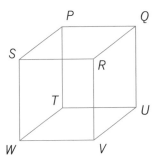

4 A small artificial ski slope is shown.
   a Find AC.
   b Find AF.
   c Find the angle between the base and AF.

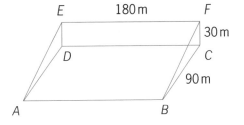

5 In the cuboid shown M is the midpoint
   of AB and N is the midpoint of HE.
   a Find angle AGE.
   b Find angle BNF.
   c Find angle HMG.

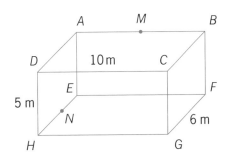

UNIT C

Theoretical probability

- **Probability** is a measure of how likely an outcome is to happen.
  - ➤ An impossible outcome has probability 0.
  - ➤ An outcome certain to happen has probability 1.
  - ➤ All other possible outcomes have probability between 0 and 1.
  - ➤ Probabilities are written as a fraction, decimal or percentage.

> If you have a probability answer greater than 1, check your calculation!

Theoretical probability can be used when outcomes are **equally likely**.

$$\text{Theoretical probability} = \frac{\text{Number of ways the outcome can happen}}{\text{Total of all possible outcomes}}$$

> Use fractions when you can, recurring and rounded decimals are less exact.

- **Mutually exclusive** events cannot happen together.
  The sum of the probabilities of mutually exclusive events is 1.
  P(event E does not happen) = 1 − P(event E does happen)

EXAMPLE

Jenny has a bag of sweets.
She chooses one sweet at random from the bag.
The probability that Jenny chooses a lime flavoured sweet = $\frac{1}{4}$.
Probability of choosing orange flavour = $\frac{3}{10}$
Probability of choosing blackcurrant flavour = $\frac{1}{6}$

Are there any other sweet flavours in the bag? Explain your answer.

$$\frac{1}{4} + \frac{3}{10} + \frac{1}{6} = \frac{15}{60} + \frac{18}{60} + \frac{10}{60} = \frac{43}{60} \neq 1$$

> If you know all the outcomes and add all their probabilities their total should equal 1.

There must be other sweet flavours in the bag to make the total probability equal 1.

EXAMPLE

A box contains only red and yellow counters.
The probability that a red counter is chosen is $\frac{1}{8}$.
a What is the probability of choosing a yellow counter?

Ian chooses first one and then another counter from the bag at random.
Both of the counters Ian chooses are red.
b What is the smallest number of yellow counters in the bag?

a If P(red) = $\frac{1}{8}$ then P(yellow) = $1 - \frac{1}{8} = \frac{7}{8}$
b There are at least 2 red counters in the bag, $\frac{1}{8} = \frac{2}{16}$

If 2 are red, then 16 − 2 = 14 are yellow, so the smallest possible number of yellow counters is 14.

Exercise CS1

1   Robert rolls a fair dice. His score on the dice is 5.
Sarah then rolls the same fair dice. What is the probability that she also scores 5?

2   A fair spinner has six equal sections.
Three sections are red, two are blue and one is purple.
   a   There are only three colours and only one section is purple.
Explain why the probability of purple is not $\frac{1}{3}$.
   b   The spinner is spun once.
Write the probability that it lands on   i   red or purple   ii   blue   iii   not blue.

3   There are some counters in a bag. They are either green or yellow.
The probability that a green counter is chosen is $\frac{5}{9}$.
   a   What is the probability of choosing a yellow counter?
One counter is taken out of the bag. It is green.
   b   What is the smallest number of yellow counters there could be in the bag?
Another counter is taken out of the bag. It is also green.
   c   Using this extra information, what is the smallest number
of yellow counters there could be in the bag?

4   I am going to take a cube from a large bag of cubes.
The probability that it is black is $\frac{1}{8}$.
There are six black cubes in the bag.
How many cubes in the bag are not black?

5   I have a large bag of lemon, orange, cherry and strawberry flavoured sweets.
I choose one sweet at random.
The table shows the probability of each flavour being chosen.

	Strawberry	Orange	Lime	Blackcurrant
Probability	x	0.4	0.15	0.25

   a   Explain why the number of lime sweets in the bag cannot be 8.
   b   There are in fact 30 lime flavoured sweets in the bag.
How many sweets in total are there in the bag?
   c   What is the probability of choosing a strawberry flavour sweet?
   d   What is the smallest possible number of each flavour of sweet in the bag?

6   Mr Todd has a series of cards with different mathematics activities:
either number, algebra, geometry or statistics.
He chooses one card at random to use with a class at the start of each week.
These are the probabilities of choosing a card for the different activities.

Mathematics	Number	Algebra	Geometry	Statistics
Probability	0.4	0.12	$3x$	x

   a   How many more cards have geometry activities than statistics?
   b   Work out the probability of choosing a geometry activity.

Listing outcomes and independent events (CS2)

- Two events are **independent** if the outcome of one event does not affect the outcome of the other event.

> Rolling two dice or one dice twice are independent events. Ten pin bowling is not as you learn as you play.

To find the overall probability of two independent events that follow on, multiply their individual probabilities.

At a road junction a cyclist can turn left, right or go straight on.
The probabilities that the cyclist turns left or right are the same.
The probability that the cyclist goes straight on is 0.4.
  a What is the probability that the cyclist turns left?
The cyclist comes to a second road junction and at this junction can turn left or right or go straight on.
The probability that the cyclist goes straight on at this junction is 0.8.
  b What is the probability that the cyclist went straight on at both road junctions?

....

  a $1 - 0.4 = 0.6$ $\frac{1}{2}$ of $0.6 = 0.3$ P(turns left) $= 0.3$

  b P(straight on and straight on) $= 0.4 \times 0.8 = 0.32$

Be systematic when listing outcomes; use a table to record all possibilities.

Reuben has two strange four-sided dice.
One dice has the numbers 2, 3, 5 and −7.
The other dice has the numbers −2, −1, 1 and 3.
Reuben rolls both dice and multiplies their scores.
  a Draw a diagram to show all possible outcomes.
  b How many outcomes are there altogether?
  c Find the probability that the outcome is   **i**   positive   **ii**   a multiple of 3.

....

  a

x	2	3	5	−7
−2	−4	−6	−10	14
−1	−2	−3	−5	7
1	2	3	5	−7
3	6	9	15	−21

  b There are 16 cells in the table, so there are 16 possible outcomes altogether.

  c i There are eight positive outcomes; 14, 7, 2, 3, 5, 6, 9 and 15.

  P(positive) $= \dfrac{8}{16} = \dfrac{1}{2}$

  ii There are seven multiples of 3: −6, −3, 3, 6, 9, 15 and −21.

  P(multiple of 3) $= \dfrac{7}{16}$

Exercise CS2

MEDIUM
HIGH

1 The pin code for a mobile phone contains the four digits 2, 3, 5 and 8.
List the different combinations that the pin code could be.

2 Jack has two marbles, one purple and one orange.
Peter has three marbles, one red, one purple and one green.
They each choose one of their own marbles.
  a List the different ways in which the marbles might be chosen.
  b What is the probability that Jack and Peter each choose
  a marble of the same colour?

3 The driving theory test has two parts, hazard warning and
multiple choice. Each part is taken independently.
Following lots of practice, Alfie finds that he passes the
hazard warning with a probability of 80% at each practice
and the multiple choice with a probability of 75% at each practice.
What is the probability that Alfie passes the driving theory test
(he must pass both parts in order to pass overall)?

4 Two spinners each have three equal sectors.
Each spinner is spun. Their scores are added
to get a total score.
  a Draw a table to show all possible total scores.
  b What is the probability that the total is:
    i 2   **ii** 5   **iii** greater than 5?

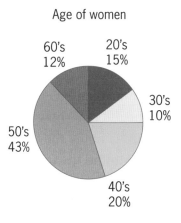

5 Two ordinary fair dice, a red dice and a green dice, are
rolled together.
What is the probability that the score on the red dice is
greater than or equal to the score on the green dice?

6 The pie charts show the ages of teachers.
One male and one female teacher are chosen
at random.
  a Find the probability that they are both
    i in their 30s   **ii** aged 50 or over.
  b If just one teacher was chosen from all
    the teachers, both men and women,
    i what additional information is
      needed to find the probability that
      the teacher is in their 40s?
    ii which age group can you write the probability for? Explain why.

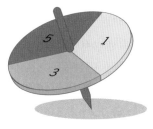

Age of men

60's 12%   20's 9%

30's 25%

50's 30%

40's 24%

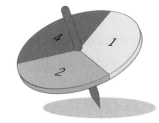

Age of women

60's 12%   20's 15%

30's 10%

50's 43%

40's 20%

Experiments and relative frequency CS3

You can **estimate probability** of an outcome by carrying out an **experiment**.

> Use an experiment:
> ➤ when finding the theoretical probability is not possible
> ➤ when you want to test theoretical probability, for example to find out if a dice is biased.

- **Relative frequency** or experimental probability = $\dfrac{\text{Number of successful trials}}{\text{Total number of trials}}$

- The greater the number of trials, the more reliable the estimate of probability.

> When there is no bias experimental and theoretical probabilities will not be exactly the same, but very close.
> Use decimals to make comparisons.

You can compare experimental probabilities with theoretical probabilities to find out if something is biased.

EXAMPLE

A spinner has four coloured sections, red, blue, yellow and green. Three students carried out an experiment to find out if the spinner was biased. Here are their results.

Student	Number of spins	Red	Blue	Yellow	Green
Ann	70	22	16	18	14
Barry	60	16	14	13	17
Carl	110	32	29	25	24

a Which student's data is likely to be the most reliable? Explain your answer.

Colour	Red	Blue	Yellow	Green
Frequency	70	59	56	55

The students collected all their results together in this table.

b Is the spinner biased? Explain your answer.

c What is the probability that the spinner lands on blue?

....

a Carl, because he has carried out a lot more trials.

b Yes, biased to red as there are a lot more reds than any other colour.

c P(blue) = $\dfrac{59}{240}$

A graph of relative frequency shows how probability changes with each trial.

EXAMPLE

Emma planted daffodils that had yellow or white petals.
She did not know how many of each colour there were.
Emma noted the colour of the petals of each daffodil as it opened.
She found the fraction of yellow daffodils each time.
This is her graph to show how the relative frequency of a daffodil with yellow petals changes with each flower.

a Use the graph to write whether the first four daffodils had yellow or white petals.

b Estimate the percentage of flowers that have white petals.

> The graph goes up each time there is a yellow daffodil and down each time the daffodil is not yellow.

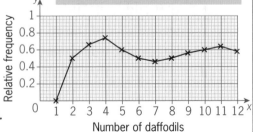

....

a White – Yellow – Yellow – Yellow

b 60%

> The value a relative frequency graph hovers around gives the best estimate of probability.

Exercise CS3

1 A spinner has ten equal sections. Each section is coloured.
The table summarises the results from 100 spins.

Colour	Red	Green	Orange	Yellow	Blue
Frequency	12	32	7	6	43

How many of each colour do you think there are? Explain your answer.

2 Four students carried out an experiment to see if a coin was biased.
Their results are summarised in the table.

	Donna	Ed	Freya	Gary
Heads	32	95	48	326
Tails	28	95	62	324

  a Whose data are likely to give the most reliable answer
to whether or not the coin is biased? Explain your answer.

  b If they collect all their results together, how many tails would there be?

  c Do you think the coin is biased or not? Explain your answer.

3 These are the scores from 20 throws of a dice.

5	2	3	3	1	6	5	3	4	2	5	6	4	3	1	2	4	5	6	1

  a Is the dice biased towards any number? Explain your answer.

  b Estimate the probability that on the next throw of the dice the score is 4.

4 Greg plays backgammon against his computer.
The graph shows the relative frequency of Greg winning.

  a Who won each of the first three games?

  b Did Greg improve at backgammon against the computer
as he continued to play? Explain your answer.

  c Estimate the probability that Greg wins the next game.

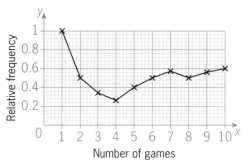

5 A spinner has five equal sections. Each section is coloured.
These are the results from 15 spins:

Red Blue Red Red Green Red Red Blue Red Green Red Green Blue Red Green

  a Draw a diagram to show the relative frequency of the spinner landing on red.

  b How many sectors do you think are coloured red?

  c The only colours obtained from the first 15 spins were red, blue and green.
Can you be certain that there is not another colour on the spinner?
Give a reason for your answer.

- Tree diagrams display all the possible results when there are several events to consider.
  - ➤ The first set of branches shows all outcomes for the first event.
  - ➤ The next sets o f branches show all outcomes for the second event.
  - ➤ The second sets are drawn from each of the first set of branches.
  - ➤ The sum of the probabilities on each set of branches is 1.
  - ➤ To find probabilities when outcomes can happen in more than one way
    - ➤ multiply the probabilities along each route

- Events are **independent** if the probability of one event does

EXAMPLE

Traffic lights operate independently of each other.

Roger drives to work each morning and passes through two sets of traffic lights.

The probability that he has to stop at the first set of lights is 0.4.

The probability that he has to stop at the second set of lights is 0.75.

a Draw a tree diagram to show all the possible outcomes.

b Calculate the probability that Roger stops at only one set of lights.

a

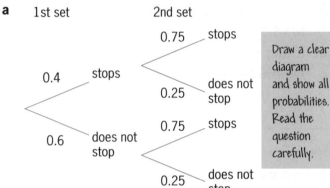

Draw a clear diagram and show all probabilities. Read the question carefully.

b P(stops only once) = P(stops, not stop)
  + P(not stop, stops)
  = (0.4 × 0.25) + (0.6 × 0.75)
  = 0.1 + 0.45 = 0.55

- The probabilities of **dependent events** depend on the outcome of a previous event.

EXAMPLE

A bag contains 8 orange and 5 lemon sweets. Tom chooses one sweet at random, eats it and then chooses a second sweet at random.

a Draw a tree diagram to show all possible outcomes.

b What is the probability that Tom chooses two sweets the same flavour?

a

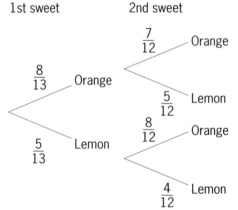

Use fractions for dependent events in a situation where something is not replaced. Remember the denominator will be one less and each pair of branches will add to 1.

b P(same flavour) = P(orange, orange) + P(lemon, lemon)

$$= \left(\frac{8}{13} \times \frac{7}{12}\right) + \left(\frac{5}{13} \times \frac{4}{12}\right) = \frac{14}{39} + \frac{5}{39} = \frac{19}{39}$$

Exercise CS4

HIGH

1 A company makes mobile phones. The probability that one of their phones is defective is 0.05.
   Two phones are chosen at random.
   a Draw a tree diagram to show all possible outcomes.
   b What is the probability that:
     i they are both defective   **ii** only one of the phones is defective?

2 Claire gets Statistics homework on a Tuesday.
   The probability that she does her Statistics homework on Tuesday evening is $\frac{3}{5}$.
   a Draw a tree diagram to show all possible outcomes of Claire doing her Statistics homework on two consecutive Tuesday evenings.
   b What is the probability that Claire does her Statistics homework on only one of two consecutive Tuesday evenings?

3 The probability that the battery in a smoke detector still works after two years is 0.7.
   There are two smoke detectors in Gareth's home.
   a Draw a tree diagram to show all possible outcomes of both smoke detectors working after two years.
   b Calculate the probability that neither battery in the smoke detectors will be working after two years.

4 Jamie either drives to work or catches the train.
   The probability that he drives to work on any one day is 0.2.
   If he drives, the probability that he arrives late is 0.7.
   If he catches the train the probability that he is late is 0.3.
   a Draw a tree diagram to show all the possible outcomes.
   b Find the probability that on a randomly chosen day Jamie is late for work.

5 Chloe is given a box of chocolates containing 10 hard centres and 15 soft centres.
   She chooses one chocolate at random, eats it and then chooses a second chocolate.
   a Draw a tree diagram to show all possible outcomes.
   b Find the probability of choosing
     i two soft centres   **ii** a soft centre and a hard centre.

6 Tom has two bags of marbles.
   In bag A there are 6 green and 2 red marbles.
   In bag B there are 3 green and 5 red marbles.
   Tom takes a marble at random from bag A and places it in bag B.
   Tom then chooses a marble at random from bag B.
   a Draw a tree diagram to show all possible outcomes.
   b Find the probability that Tom chooses a marble of different colours from each bag.
   c Suppose Tom had chosen a marble from bag B first, placed it in bag A and then chosen a marble from bag A; what would your probability be now for Tom to choose marbles of different colours from each bag?

UNIT C

GCSE formulae

In your OCR GCSE examination you will be given a formula sheet like the one on this page.
You should use it as an aid to memory. It will be useful to become familiar with the information on this sheet.

Volume of a prism = area of cross section × length

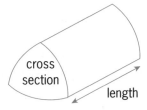

Volume of sphere = $\frac{4}{3} \pi r^3$
Surface area of sphere = $4 \pi r^2$

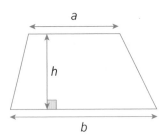

Volume of cone = $\frac{1}{3} \pi r^2 h$
Curved surface area of cone = $\pi r l$

Area of trapezium = $\frac{1}{2}(a + b)h$

In any triangle ABC

Sine rule $\dfrac{a}{\sin A} = \dfrac{b}{\sin B} = \dfrac{c}{\sin C}$

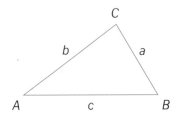

Cosine rule $a^2 = b^2 + c^2 - 2bc \cos A$

Area of triangle = $\frac{1}{2} ab \sin C$

The Quadratic Equation
The solutions of $ax^2 + bx + c = 0$
where $a \neq 0$, are given by
$$x = \frac{-b \pm \sqrt{(b^2 - 4ac)}}{2a}$$

Unit A Higher Practice Paper

60 marks   **1 hour**

1 a Share £168 in the ratio 5 : 7.   [2 marks]

 b Write the ratio 45 : 60 in its simplest form.   [1 mark]

 c A bag of flour has been divided in the ratio 1 : 6 : 3.
   The largest share weighs 1.8 kg.
   What was the weight of the original bag
   of flour?   [2 marks]

 d A model train is made to a scale of 1 : 30.
   Copy and complete this statement using a fraction.
   The height of the model train is $\frac{1}{30}$th ___ of the height
   of the real train.   [1 mark]

 e A fruit cocktail is made using Orange, Apple and
   Lemonade in the ratio 2 : 3 : 10.
   Copy and complete this statement using a fraction.
   Orange is ___ 2/15 ___ of the contents of the fruit
   cocktail.   [1 mark]

2 Solve

 a $3x - 5 = 43$ (+5) $3x = 47$ $x =$ [2 marks]

 b $12 = 5 + \dfrac{x}{5}$ (÷3)(÷3)   [2 marks]

 c $2(x - 2) = 5(2x - 7)$ [3 marks]

3 Insert brackets into the following calculations so that they are correct.

 a $8 + 3 \times 4 - 1 \times 2 = 26$ [1 mark]

 b $8 + 3 \times 4 - 1 \times 2 = 22$ [2 marks]

4 a Draw the fourth term in this sequence of dot patterns.

[1 mark]

term 1   term 2   term 3   term 4

 b Write down the nth term of the sequence.   [2 marks]

 c Rachel draws a sequence of dot patterns that has an nth
   term $= 5n - 6$.
   Show that it is impossible for two patterns to be in the
   same term in Rachel's sequence and the sequence in **part a**
   and both to have the same number of dots.   [4 marks]

5   This is a parallelogram, **ABCD**.
    Use ruler and compasses only to construct the region that is
    inside the parallelogram and:
    • Closer to **A** than **C** and,
    • Closer to **AB** than **BC**.   [3 marks]

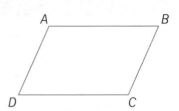

6   Joseph has an electricity meter that records the number of
    day units and the number of night units that he uses.
    He uses three times as many day units as night units.
    A day unit is 35 pence more than one night unit.
    In a period when he uses 620 units his electricity
    bill is £274.35.
    Find the cost of a night unit.   [4 marks]

7   **a** Expressed as the product of its prime factors, $36 = 2^2 × 3^2$.
       Express 42 as the product of its prime factors.   [2 marks]
    b What is the least common multiple of
       36 and 42?   [1 mark]

8   The table shows the numbers of minutes that flights from
    a small airport were delayed in one day. No flights were
    delayed more than 100 minutes.

Number of minutes delay	Number of flights
0 to 20	5
21 to 40	6
41 to 60	2
61 to 80	3
81 to 100	4

    Calculate an estimate of the mean number of minutes that a
    flight had been delayed.   [4 marks]

9   Karen has these metal strips.
    She needs to join three of them to make a right-angled
    triangle to support a structure she is making.

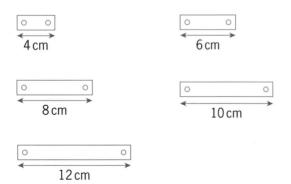

    Show how Karen can do this.   [4 marks]

10 *NewBatt* have produced two types of battery, *A* and *B*.
They test a sample of each type of battery and record how
many hours each battery lasts. These are the results.

Type A (numbers of hours)

70	72	72	74	80	85	89	90	90	91	91	92	93	93	94
96	96	96	98	100	102	105	105	105	108	110	115	116	116	120

Type B (numbers of hours)

75	75	76	78	78	86	91	92	92	93	94	94	94
94	96	96	98	100	102	102	105	106	110	120	126	130

Represent the data with a suitable diagram and compare
the performance of the two types of battery.   [6 marks]

11 A pencil pot is made by attaching a plastic cylinder to a
square, plastic base.

A diagonal of the cylinder is 18 cm so that a new pencil will
just fit inside the pot.
The pot needs to be stable so should not be too narrow.
Calculate a possible angle between the diagonal and the
base of the cylinder and give the radius and height of the
cylinder.
You must show working and state your reasons.   [6 marks]

12 These distributions of weights of female cats owned by men
and by women were recorded by a vet. No cat weighed less
than 1.5 kg and no cat weighed above 5.5 kg.

Key □ = 10 cats

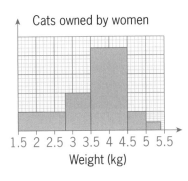

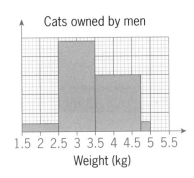

Should the vet target men or women with advice on healthy
feeding for their cats?
You must support your answer with evidence
from the graphs.   [6 marks]

60 marks **1 hour** **No calculator**

1 Khalid is going on holiday in his car.
   He has this information.

Number of miles travelled on one gallon of fuel	43.8
Length of journey (in miles)	2130
Number of litres in one gallon	4.5
Cost of one litre of fuel in pence	111.9

Calculate an estimate of the cost, in pounds, of the fuel
Khalid will use.   [4 marks]

2 a State the value of $\dfrac{5^2 \times 5^3}{5^5}$ [2 marks]

   b Simplify
      i $2g - 2 \times 4g^3$ [2 marks]
      ii $\dfrac{4}{\sqrt{4g^8}}$ [2 marks]

3 The diagram shows a parallelogram, *ABCD*, drawn between
   two parallel lines, *PQ* and *RS*.
   Angle *ADC* = 50° and angle *CBQ* = 75°.

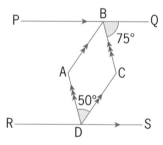

   Not to scale

   a Calculate the size of reflex angle *DAB*.   [2 marks]
   b Explain why angle *ABP* = 55°.   [2 marks]

4 a Draw the graph of $y = 6 - 2x$ for values of x, $-3 \le x \le 5$.
                                                      [3 marks]

   b Write down the gradient of $y = 6 - 2x$ [1 mark]
   c Will the line $y = 6 - 2x$ pass through
      the point $(-50, 94)$?
   Show working to support your answer.   [2 marks]

5 The diagram shows a triangle A and a square P.

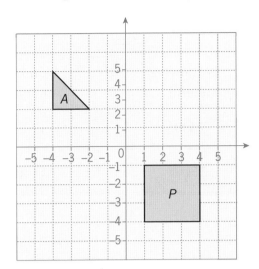

P is made by joining two triangles. Each triangle is a
transformation of triangle **A**.
Describe fully the transformations required to
create square **P**. [6 marks]

6 Calculate, writing each answer as a mixed number in the
simplest possible form.

a $\dfrac{1}{3} + 1\dfrac{1}{9}$ [3 marks]

b $\dfrac{2}{3} \div 1\dfrac{1}{9}$ [3 marks]

7 The length of one side of this square, drawn on a one
centimetre square dotty grid, is $\sqrt{2}$ cm.

a Write down the exact value for the perimeter
of the square.
Give your answer in its simplest form. [1 mark]
b Use this dotty grid to show that the area of the
square is $2\,\text{cm}^2$.

[3 marks]

8 a Brian has kept this record of the number of units of electricity he used in each **quarter** (three months) for the last three years.

2007	Number of units	2008	Number of units	2009	Number of units	2010	Number of units
Spring	2400	Spring	2100	Spring	2000	Spring	1800
Summer	1800	Summer	1800	Summer	1500	Summer	1400
Autumn	2100	Autumn	2000	Autumn	1800	Autumn	
Winter	2800	Winter	2600	Winter	2400	Winter	

    i   Copy and complete this time series graph.
The first ten figures have been plotted for you. [2 marks]

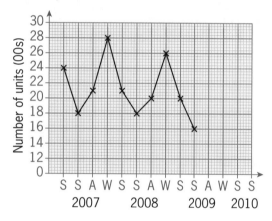

    ii Draw a trend line on your graph.   [1 mark]
    iii Use the graph to estimate the number of units Brian might use in the Autumn quarter of 2010.   [2 marks]

b Brian asks two electricity companies, Prolec and Ecost, for information about their prices.
He draws this graph showing how much electricity from the two companies will cost as he uses more units.
Brian will pay for the electricity he uses each month.

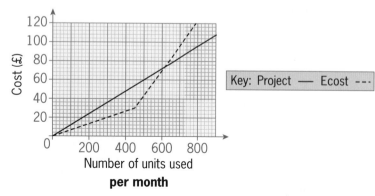

Use the graphs to recommend a company for Brian to use.
                   [4 marks]

9 This shows the sum of two vectors.

$$\begin{pmatrix} 4a \\ 2a \end{pmatrix} + \begin{pmatrix} 3b \\ b \end{pmatrix} = \begin{pmatrix} 1 \\ -1 \end{pmatrix}$$

Find the value of a and the value of b. [4 marks]

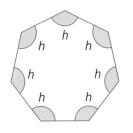

10 a The diagram shows a regular heptagon with each interior angle = h.

Explain why h cannot be a whole number.
No marks will be given for an answer that relies upon measurements. [2 marks]

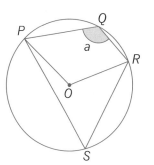

b The diagram shows a quadrilateral $PQRS$ inscribed within a circle.

Two lines PO and RO are shown.

The centre of the circle is O and angle $PQR = $ **a**.

Prove that angle $PQR = 180° - $ angle PSR. [3 marks]

11 Amy has collected this data on petrol engines.

Manufacturer	Engine size	Carbon (grams per km)
Alfa Romeo	3.2	289
Peugeot	3.0	233
Ford	2.8	259
Ford	2.3	242
Alfa Romeo	2.2	221
Peugeot	2.2	214
Alfa Romeo	2.0	211

Manufacturer	Engine size	Carbon (grams per km)
Audi	2.0	192
Alfa Romeo	1.9	205
Ford	1.8	169
Audi	1.8	174
BMW	1.8	140
Alfa Romeo	1.6	194
Ford	1.6	154

Manufacturer	Engine size	Carbon (grams per km)
BMW	1.6	179
Toyota	1.5	104
Ford	1.4	145
Ford	1.3	141
Ford	1.25	139
Daihatsu	1.0	114

Amy thinks that the size of the engine used in a car has an effect on the amount of carbon that the car produces.

Use the data to test Amy's idea and comment on your results.

You may wish to draw a graph. [6 marks]

100 marks   **2 hours**

1 Jean has £12 000 to invest for one year.
She sees these two accounts.

> **ONE-YEAR BOND**
>
> 4% interest paid on the account at the end of the year.

> **HALF-YEAR ACCOUNT**
>
> 2% interest added to the account after 6 months.
> 2% paid on all savings at the end of the year.

The company claims that the half-year account pays much more interest than the one-year bond.
Is this claim justified?   [6 marks]

2 **a** Expand $3a(2a + 1)$ [2 marks]
b Expand and simplify $2x(x - 2) - (x + 2)$ [3 marks]
c Factorise $4x^2 - 9y^2$ [1 mark]

3 Rashid wants to calculate the amount of fat he will eat if he has his favourite cereal for breakfast every day for a year.
The cereal has 11.8 g of fat in an average serving, with milk.
His calculations are set out below.

1 week $= 7 \times 11.8$ $= 82.6$ g
1 month $= 82 \times 4 = 328$ g
1 year $= 12 \times 330$ $= 3960$ g or 3.96 kg.

Explain what Rashid has done wrong.   [2 marks]

4 Paul deals one hand of five cards to himself and one hand to Jenny.

  Paul

  Jenny

They do not look at the cards but each turns one card over at random.
King (K) scores 13 points and Ace (A) scores 14 points.

a Copy and complete this diagram to show the cards they could turn over. [2 marks]

b What is the probability that the cards turned over are of equal value? [2 marks]

c What is the probability that Paul's card is worth more than Jenny's? [2 marks]

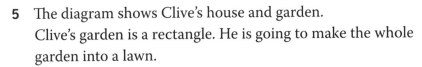

5 The diagram shows Clive's house and garden.
Clive's garden is a rectangle. He is going to make the whole garden into a lawn.

He measures the length = 40 m and the width = 18 m both **correct to the nearest metre**.

Not to scale

a What is the smallest possible length the garden could be? [1 mark]

b Clive needs 40g of grass seed for each square metre of lawn.
How many square metres of lawn will one 5 kg bag of seed cover? [2 marks]

c* Explain why measuring the length and width of his garden to the nearest metre will not affect the price Clive pays so that he has enough seed for his lawn. [6 marks]

6 a Expand and simplify $(x + 3)(x - 1)$ [2 marks]

b i Factorise $x^2 + 10x - 24$ [2 marks]

ii Using your result to **part (b)(i)** or otherwise, solve $x^2 + 10x = 24$ [2 marks]

7 Lisa makes this open box.
She cuts the net from this sheet of paper (each small square is 1cm²).

a Show how the net may be made by cutting just four squares from the sheet of paper. [1 mark]

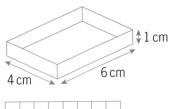

b Graham said, 'Any open box you make from that piece of paper will have the same surface area and volume.'
Show whether Graham is right or wrong. [4 marks]

8 Use your calculator to work out

a $\sqrt{3.7^2 + 2.31}$ **b** $\dfrac{1.2 + 4.3^2}{5.6^2 - 10.36}$ [2 marks]

Write your answer to 2 significant figures. [3 marks]

c $\dfrac{(1.5 \times 10^4) + (2.3 \times 10^{-2})}{(4.7 \times 10^4)}$

Give your answer in standard index form to an appropriate level of accuracy. [3 marks]

9 A cuboid is twice as long as it is high.

The width of the cuboid is 8 centimetres more than the height.

The area of the largest face of the cuboid is 120 cm².

Find the height of the cuboid, correct to 1 decimal place.

[6 marks]

10 When a pendulum is released the time it takes to swing from the starting position and back again is called the period.

The period, T seconds, can be calculated using the formula

$$T = 2\pi\sqrt{\frac{l}{g}}$$

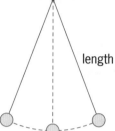

point of suspension

length

l = length of pendulum (metres),

g = acceleration due to gravity, m/s²

a Calculate T when $l = 1.6 \times 104$ mm and $g = 10$ m/s².

Do not substitute a value for π in your calculation.

[3 marks]

b* The value 10 m/s² is an approximation that overestimates the value of g.

Explain how using a more accurate value for g will affect your answer for **part (a)**. [2 marks]

c Rearrange the formula $T = 2\pi\sqrt{\frac{l}{g}}$ to make l the subject. [3 marks]

11 Geoff uses a road that has an automatic railway crossing.

The crossing closes 35 seconds before a train arrives and opens immediately it has passed.

A train takes 10 seconds to pass.

If another train is close enough to arrive in 35 seconds the crossing stays closed.

The line is busy and the probability that the crossing is closed by a train is 0.1.

The probability that a second train arrives whilst the gate is closed is 0.05.

The probability that a third train arrives whilst the gate is closed is 0.01.

The probability that a fourth train arrives whilst the gate is closed is 0.

a Copy and complete this tree diagram.

[2 marks]

b What is the probability that Geoff waits no more than 45 seconds at the crossing? [1 mark]

c What is the probability that Geoff waits no more than 90 seconds at the crossing? [2 marks]

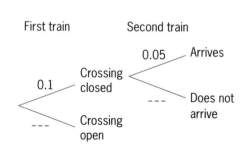

First train

Second train

0.05 — Arrives

Crossing
0.1 — closed

— — — Does not arrive

— — — Crossing open

d What is the probability that Geoff waits more than
   90 seconds at the crossing? [2 marks]

e Geoff arrives as the crossing is closing and waits for
   three trains to pass. Explain why Geoff may not wait
   135 seconds to cross. [2 marks]

f Explain why it is not possible to state the probability
   that Geoff waits 60 seconds at the crossing. [2 marks]

12

"...and here is the news. The Financial Times Index has fallen by 6%. Its value is now 546."

What was the value of the Financial Times Index
before the fall? [2 marks]

13 A wooden wheel is made using 8 sections of hickory wood
attached by spokes to a central hub, as shown. Each section
holds two spokes.
There is a steel tyre around the rim, which is 1 cm thick.
The central hole for the axle has a diameter of 8 cm.
The hub is 6 cm thick.
Each spoke is 18 cm long and tapers from 3 cm thick at the
hub to 2cm thick at the rim.
The wooden rim is 6 cm thick.

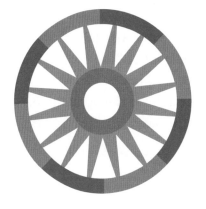

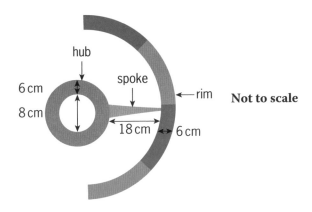

Not to scale

a What is the diameter of the wheel, including
   the tyre? [1 mark]

b If the wheel is symmetrical, what is the gap between
   the nearest edges of each spoke where they
   meet the hub? [3 marks]

c The steel tyre just fits the wooden rim and is 7.5 cm
   wide.
   1 cm³ of hickory wood has a weight of 0.88 g.
   What is the weight of one section of the
   wooden rim? [5 marks]

14 The curve shown on the axes is for the function
$x^2 + y^2 = 16$.

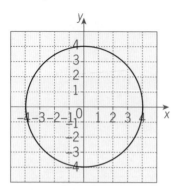

   a Copy the graph and draw, on the same axes, the curve for
the function $x^2 + y^2 = 25$. [2 marks]

   b Draw, on the same axes, the graph of $y = 2x$. [1 mark]

   c Show how the graphs may be used to
solve $5x^2 = 16$. [4 marks]

15 A pyramid $ABCDE$ stands on a rectangular base.
The length of the base, BC, is 25 cm and the width,
AB, is 14 cm.
The apex of the pyramid, E, is 20 cm above the centre
of the base, F.

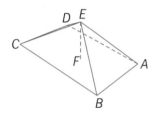

   a Calculate the angle between AE and the
base ABCD. [3 marks]

   b Calculate the area of the face AEB. [6 marks]

Answers

Unit A

Ex AN1

1 a + × – is – **b** + ÷ – is –
  c – × – × – = + × – = – **d** + × – = –
2 192 **3** 19°C **4 a** 89p **b** 90p
5 a 330 mm **b** 47.1 mm **c** 25.7 mm
  d The height growth rate of boys is almost double that of girls between 11 and 18. However, girls start their growth in puberty earlier than 11 as shown by the fact that they are taller than boys on average at the beginning of the time period analysed
6 9091 km

Ex AN2

1 a eleven thousand, three hundred and eighty-four
  b two million, ten thousand, three hundred and forty-five
  c four million, five hundred thousand and twenty
  d twenty three million, four hundred and forty four thousand and twelve
2 a 12 609 **b** 50 120 007 **c** 142.2 **d** 15 905 053
3 a 12.3$\underline{7}$6 **b** 0.00$\underline{4}$69 **c** 25.09$\underline{3}$6 **d** 3.5$\underline{3}$98
4 a 12.38 **b** 0.0 **c** 25.094 **d** 3.54
5 a 12.376 **b** 0.00469 **c** 25.0936 **d** 3.5398
6 a 140 300 **b** 30 000 **c** 0.6 **d** 17.1
  e 50 000 **f** 1.97 **g** 3 **h** 0.003
  i 825.77 **j** 17.0
7 a 1.7 **b** 21 **c** 0.14 **d** 7.7
8 £19.18
9 a £28.38 **b** 231 **c** 12p **d** 20p **e** £17.82

Ex AN3

1 a 6.25 **b** 25 **c** 0.784 **d** 11 **e** 3
  f 4.79 **g** 3.3 **h** 0.1 **i** −154.7
2 a 0.2 **b** 5 **c** 0.08$\dot{3}$ **d** 0.01 **e** 0.0$\dot{5}$ **f** 12.8
  a and **b** are reciprocals of one another
3 a £2.60 **b** £25.98
4 a 4200 mm **b** 1060 m
  c yes – the bracket is 100 mm wide which is more than half the width of the shelf
  d No – the drive would need to be 163.4 m long
5 a 22.4 km **b** 20 miles
6 1044 grams

Ex AN4

1 a 19.5 **b** 2.9 **c** 9.8
  d −5.2 **e** −0.8 **f** 36.4
2 b 4 − 3 ÷ 2 = 4 − 1.5 = 2.5
  c (1 + 4) × 3 − 6 = 15 − 6 = 9
  d 4 − 2 × (3 + 1) = 4 − 8 = −4
  e 3 − (2 × 1.5 + 1) = 3 − 4 = −1
  f 12 + 2(3 × 4) − 2 = 12 + 24 − 2 = 34
3 a 5 **b** 5.8 **c** 9.25 **d** 0.7
  e 9 **f** 4.1 **g** 4.2 **h** 49
4 a (1 + 2) × 3 = 9 **b** 1 + 2 × (3 − 4) = −1
  c 10 − (3 + 2) × 5 = −15 **d** (10 − 3 + 2) × 5 = 45
  e 10 − (3 + 2 × 5) = −3 **f** (14 + 5) × 2² = 76
  g 14 + (5 × 2)² = 114 **h** 12 − (2 + 5 × 2) + 1 = 1

5 a No **b** £25 + £15 × 3 **c** £70

Ex AN5

1 a 6, 12, 18, 24, 30 **b** 8, 16, 24, 32, 40
  c 17, 34, 51, 68, 85 **d** 23, 46, 69, 92, 115
  e 51, 102, 153, 204, 255 **f** 242, 484, 726, 968, 1210
2 a 1, 2, 4, 8, 16 **b** 1, 3, 7, 21
  c 1, 2, 3, 4, 6, 9, 12, 18, 36 **d** 1, 43
  e 1, 2, 3, 4, 5, 6, 8, 10, 12, 15, 20, 24, 30, 40, 60, 120
  f 1, 2, 3, 4, 6, 8, 12, 23, 24, 46, 69, 92, 138, 184, 276, 552
3 31, 37, 41, 43, 47
4 a no **b** yes **c** no **d** no **e** no **f** yes
5 a $2 \times 3 \times 5$ **b** $2^3 \times 3^2$ **c** 2×7^2
  d $2 \times 5 \times 13$ **e** 2×83 **f** 2^{10}
6 a 60 **b** 48 **c** 132 **d** 60 **e** 180
7 a 6 **b** 8 **c** 2 **d** 1 **e** 3
8 10 o'clock

Ex AN6

1 a 2:3 **b** 4:3 **c** 2:3 **d** 3:1
  e 2:3:4 **f** 5:2:6 **g** 4:1:3 **h** 3:4
  i 24:3:8 **j** 10:1
2 a 1:4 **b** 1:0.5 **c** 1:1.5
  d 1:2.5 **e** 1:0.2 **f** 1:0.22
3 a 1.25:1 **b** 0.4:1 **c** 1.25:1
  d $1\frac{2}{3}:1$ **e** 6:1 **f** 0.875:1
4 a 5:12 **b** 1:300 **c** 1:5
  d 20:1 **e** 1:7 **f** 1:48
5 a 8:3:6 **b** 8:12:1 **c** 1:2:10
  d 2:1:50 **e** 480:1:110 **f** 30:2:9
6 a $\frac{2}{5}$ **b** $\frac{1}{2}$ **c** $\frac{5}{9}$ **d** $\frac{1}{2}$ **e** $\frac{2}{5}$ **f** $\frac{4}{15}$

Ex AN7

1 a £5:£20 **b** 140 g:60 g **c** 1.05 kg:1.75 kg
  d 100 mins:60 mins:20 mins
2 a 8.1 kg **b** £10.25 **c** 72p
  d W = 0.5 litres, X = 7.5 litres
3 a i £60.75 **ii** £109.35 **b** £1458
4 a 36 m² **b** $\frac{2}{9}$
5 a 2.5 g **b** 35:6 **c** 2:3
  d there is $1\frac{1}{2}$ times as much fibre as fat
  e Fat equals 0.096 of the biscuit which is less than 0.1 or $\frac{1}{10}$. Therefore TRUE.
6 a 630 miles **b** Yes – he claims £336
7 a Hint 25:3
  b 1.875 litres of red and 1.125 litres of white
  c Pale **d** 5.6 litres

Ex AA1

1 a $4y$ **b** c^4 **c** $8s − 3t$
  d $12z^3$ **e** $−g − 9h$ **f** 0
2 a equation **b** identity **c** formula
  d formula **e** equation **f** identity
3 a 20 **b** 4 **c** 36
  d 22 **e** 108
4 a $11a + 6b$ **b** $2t + 26$ **c** $x − 12y$
  d $p^2 + 14p$ **e** $20xy$ **f** $7ab$

5 Abdul

6 a $28mn$ **b** $12m^2$ **c** $10p$ **d** 2
 e $24abc$ **f** $6k^3$ **g** $4b$ **h** $9c$

7

4p +7q	4p +7q	**4p +2q**
6mn	**10mn**	6mn
2d	**2**	2d
2n − 8	**2n**	2n − 8

8 a i $8p +16$ **ii** $32p$ **b** $3x, 2y$

Ex AA2

1 a $4c + 20$ **b** $7y + 49$ **c** $p^2 - 7p$
 d $y^2 + yz$ **e** $2e^2 + 10ef$ **f** $9f^2 + 12hf$
2 a $5(h - 4)$ **b** $7(4 + k)$ **c** $f(f + 9)$
 d $4(y + 3)$ **e** $6(3d - 4)$ **f** $20(2 - 3m)$
 g $q(p - q)$ **h** $3g(g + 2)$ **i** $4n(2m + 3n)$

Ex AA3

1 i a $(2.5, 3)$ **b** $(4, 2)$ **c** $(2.5, -1)$
 d $(-1, -2)$ **e** $(-1, 5.5)$ **f** $(3.5, -1)$
 ii a 5 **b** 7.21 **c** 9.22
 d 6.32 **e** 17 **f** 7.28
2 a $(5, -4)$ **b** $M = (0, 1)$ $N = (4, 3)$
 $$MN = \sqrt{(4-0)^2 + (3-1)^2}$$
 $$= \sqrt{4^2 + 2^2} = \sqrt{16+4} = \sqrt{20}$$

Ex AA4

1 a -21 **b** -18 **c** -108
 d 8.49 **e** 0.5 **f** 7.17
2 a $C = \pounds(pw + 4)$ **b** $A = \frac{1}{2}\pi r^2 - 3vh$
3 a $x = \dfrac{y - c}{m}$ **b** $x = \dfrac{t + 9}{w}$ **c** $x = \dfrac{s - ab}{r}$
 d $x = \dfrac{q}{r + z}$ **e** $x = 3m - f$ **f** $x = \dfrac{y}{p}$
 g $x = t(c + d)$ **h** $x = \dfrac{5w - 7}{k} - w$ **i** $x = \sqrt{\dfrac{z}{y}}$
 j $x = \sqrt{dc - a}$ **k** $x = r^2 - a$ **l** $x = \dfrac{m^2 - b}{a}$
4 a $t = \dfrac{d}{3 - m}$ **b** $t = \dfrac{7 - f}{r + 2}$ **c** $t = \dfrac{2m - 3p}{6 - d}$
 d $t = \dfrac{rs}{r - 1}$ **e** $t = \dfrac{12a}{m + a - 5}$ **f** $t = \dfrac{5g + 9}{5 - g}$
 g $t = \dfrac{3}{p - 3}$ **h** $t = \dfrac{12k}{12 - k}$
5 a $a = \dfrac{A}{\pi b}$ **b** 94.2cm^2
 A stamping machine has to leave gaps between the ellipses

Ex AA5

1 a 16, 21 **b** 8, 15 **c** 10, 20 **d** 1.6, 1.8
 e 10, 8 **f** 20, 0 **g** 2, 6 **h** 0, 4
2 a 87 **b** 0
3 a

 b

Pattern	1	2	3	4
No. of squares	3	5	7	9

 c 201
4 $5n + 1$

5 a Because the length of the spring goes up by the
 same amount each time
 b $3.5n + 34.5$ cm **c** 19
6 $k = -1$; 13

Ex AA6

1 a 5 **b** 4 **c** 3.5 **d** 3 **e** -4
 f -3 **g** 6 **h** -2 **i** -19
2 a $x = 12$; angles are 60°, 120°, 60°, 120°
 b parallelogram
3 a 3 **b** 6 **c** 28
 d $-\dfrac{1}{2}$ **e** -3 **f** -13
4 a i $x + 10$ **ii** $2x + 20$ **b** $4x + 30 = 182$; 38
5 a $10(x - 4) + 2(3x + 5) + 5(20 - x) = 180$; $x = 10$
 b 60°, 70°, 50° **c** Acute angled or scalene
6 a $LHS = 4 \times 1 = 4$, but $RHS = 6 - 2 \times 11 = -16$
 b -2×5 is -10 not $+10$ **c** $x = 0$

Ex AG1

1 a 3000 g **b** 3.5 cm **c** 400 cm
 d 0.6 litres **e** 48 pints **f** 42 inches
 g 38.5 lbs **h** $1\frac{1}{2}$ ft **i** 1 stone 5 lbs
 j 8 ft 6 inches
2 a 120 cm **b** $7\frac{1}{2}$ kg **c** 18 litres **d** 6 litres
3 a $6\frac{2}{3}$ ft **b** 15.6 miles **c** 26.4 lbs **d** 28 pints
4 253 km
5 a 175 cm **b** 1.75 m
6 14 lb 2 oz
7 6 pints
8 Yes – it is 4.8 m by 2.4 m
9 a 108 000 litres **b** 60 hours
10 £6360 (3 s.f.)

Ex AG2

1 Standard constructions
2 Standard constructions
3 36.9°, 53.1°, 90°. Right angled
4 6.1 cm
5 72°
6 Standard constructions
7 Standard constructions

Ex AG3

1

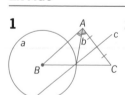

2 a Perpendicular bisector of XZ
 b Angle bisector of angle ZWX
 c

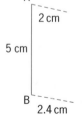

3

A
2 cm
5 cm
B
2.4 cm

4 a

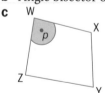

b **i** 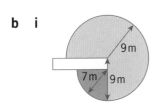 **ii**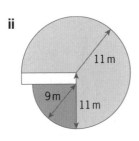

Ex AG4

1 a 250° **b** 325° **c** 110°
2 a West **b** North East **c** North West
3 020°
4 a Travel 9 km on a bearing of 035°, then 6 km on a bearing of 115°
b 15 km. Direct distance = 11.7 km
5 a 50 km **b** 0.29 cm **c** 417.5 km
6 A typical house frontage is 20 m. The scale given converts 1 cm to 60 km, so 20 m would be too small on the scale drawing.
On a plan, need 20 m to convert to about 20 cm, i.e. a scale of 1 : 100

Ex AG5

1 a 4.2 m **b** 9.1 m **c** 12.2 m **d** 18.3 m
2 14.1 m
3 10.1 inches
4 471.7 m
5 a 8.6 units **b** $\sqrt{(p-r)^2 + (q-t)^2}$
6 No because $7^2 + 15^2 \neq 17^2$
7 72 m²
8 $x = 7.6$ cm, $y = 7.9$ cm
9 6.7 cm
10 25.98 m

Ex AG6

1 a 5.63 cm **b** 13.23 cm **c** 34.85°
d 30.07° **e** 10.68 cm
2 45.2°
3 58.4°
4 56.4 m
5 40.6 m
6 a 7.70 m **b** 9.72 m **c** 2 metres approx

Ex AS1

1

	Red	Blue	Green	Black	Silver	Other
Car						
Lorry						
Bus or coach						
Van						
Other						

2

		Shoe sizes					
		3	4	5	6	7	8
Glove sizes	XS						
	Small		9				
	Medium			7			
	large						

3 a 1 she only asked people who live in her local area
    2 she did it on a Tuesday morning so did not include those at work
b choose a random sample from the electoral register and do a door to door or postal survey of these people

4 a does not include all hair colours e.g. red; does not distinguish between natural hair colour and dyed hair colours.
Should ask "What colour is your hair at the moment?"
Blonde Brown Black Red Other
b OK
c This is subjective – need to have some accurate way of describing short, medium and long hair for both men and women
d Need 2 extra categories : Less than once a week
More than twice but not every day
e Would be better to ask "How often do you use conditioner?"
Always Sometimes Never
5 It could end up being biased towards a particular gender or age group. Better to stratify sample by year group and gender.

Ex AS2

1 a i 9 **ii** 9 **b** 8.8
2 a £35.38 **b** £30.38
3 The mode as that is an actual size (7) and is the most frequent sale. Note that the median is also 7, but the mean is approx 6.98 which is not an actual shoe size.
4 a 68.6 mins **b** $60 < m \leqslant 80$
c there is not a prominent modal class.
There are 3 very distinct peaks in the data with very similar frequencies
5 a May 3.8 hours   June 4.4 hours
b i May $2 \leqslant h < 4$ June $4 \leqslant h < 6$
ii May $2 \leqslant h < 4$ June $4 \leqslant h < 6$

Ex AS3

1

0	9
1	1 5 6
2	0 2 3 4 8 9
3	0 1 2 4
4	1

2

1	8 8
2	1 2 4 4 5 5 7 8
3	4 6 7 9
4	0 1 3 6
5	
6	0
7	5

Key 2|3 means 23 minutes.   Key 3|7 means 3700

3 The median for Species *B* is 52 mm whereas that for Species *A* is 48 mm, so Species *B* is longer on average.
The range for *B* is 72 – 29 = 43 mm and for *A*: 75 – 21 = 54 mm, which suggests that there is greater variation of length in Species *A*.
The *IQR* for *B* = 58 – 36 = 22 mm and for *A*, the *IQR* = 63 – 34 = 29 mm, so this is even stronger evidence of greater variation of length in Species *A*.

4 a

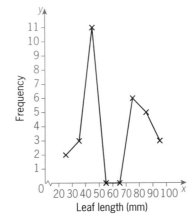

Leaf length (mm)

b Because there appears to be 2 different distributions, one with a modal class of $40 < l \leqslant 50$ and the other with a modal class of $70 < l \leqslant 80$.

5 a

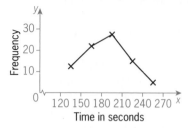

b The modal class for the swim to bike transition is 180 to 210 secs, whereas the modal class for the bike to run transition is 90 to 120 secs. On average, the swim to bike transition is roughly twice as long.

Ex AS4

1 The median age for the Winter Craft Fair is much higher (20 years older). The ranges are similar, but the *IQR* for the Winter Craft Fair is much larger showing that the ages of those attending are far more diverse.

2 a

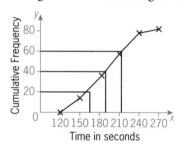

b

	Swim to bike	Bike to run
Median	188 secs	92 secs
IQR	213 − 162 = 51 secs	115 − 68 = 47 secs

It takes on average roughly twice as long for the swim to bike transition, but the variability in the times is very similar for both transitions.

3 a

Time in mins	CF
0	0
4	6
8	24
12	48
16	94
20	158
24	188
28	200

b

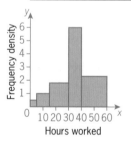

c i 36   **ii** 200 − 172 = 28
d Median = 16.4 mins   *UQ* = 19.6 mins
  LQ = 12.2 mins

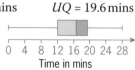

4 a

Time in mins	CF
22	0
30	18
40	60
50	103
60	115
68	120

b

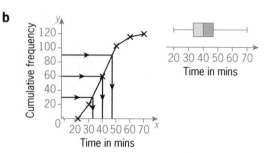

Ex AS5

1 a Estimate last group as $30 < u \leqslant 50$. Represent first group as $-1 < u \leqslant 0$.

Units(u)	$-1 < u \leqslant 0$	$0 < u \leqslant 1$	$1 < u \leqslant 7$	$7 < u \leqslant 15$	$15 < u \leqslant 30$	$30 < u \leqslant 50$
Class width	1	1	6	8	15	20
Frequency density	8	12	4.5	3.75	1.4	0.45

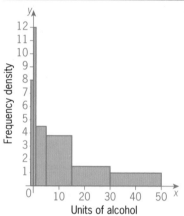

b 8 + 12 + 27 + 30 + 1.4 x 6 ≈ 85

2 a

Class width	6	9	15	12	18
Frequency density	0.5	1	1.8	5.75	2.33

b 2 × 5.75 + 42 ≈ 54
c Number of women working 6 to 15 hours per week = 5 × 9 = 45
  Number of women working 15 to 30 hours per week = 3 × 15 = 45
d The modal class for men is 30 − 42 hours per week, whereas for women it is 6 − 15 hours per week. The data for men has negative skew, whereas that for women has positive skew.

3 a

Time (mins)	$0 < t \leqslant 20$	$20 < t \leqslant 30$	$30 < t \leqslant 40$	...
Number	10	16	32	...

Complete the histogram with bar heights (frequency density) of

$40 < t \leqslant 45$	5.6
$45 < t \leqslant 60$	2.2
$60 < t \leqslant 90$	0.7

b 2.2 × 10 + 21 = 43

Unit B

Ex BN1

1
- **a** 13.9
- **b** 7.1
- **c** 4.76
- **d** 6.1
- **e** 15.2
- **f** 4.64
- **g** 1.26
- **h** 10.16
- **i** 33.26

2
- **a** 49.2
- **b** 13.5
- **c** 4.52
- **d** 0.625
- **e** 22
- **f** 31.6
- **g** 15.6
- **h** 400
- **i** 110
- **j** 229
- **k** 0.296
- **l** 7.98

3 **a** 2.7 **b** 1.5 **c** 27 **d** 15 **e** 150

4 14 miles

5 21.7 mg

6 **a** 269.6 km **b** 98 km **c** 4.6 km

7 5.7 km

8 46

Ex BN2

1 **a**, **c**, **d** are clearly wrong

2
- **a** 13.3
- **b** 0.01
- **c** 5.01
- **d** 102 000
- **e** 0.30
- **f** 9.1

3
- **a** $12.6 + 2.7 = 15.3$
- **b** $71 + 5 = 76$
- **c** $0.25 \times 10 \div 2 = 2.5 \div 2 = 1.25$
- **d** $4.1 \times 5 = 20.5$
- **e** $(4 + 2) \div 6 = 1$
- **f** $3 \times 1.5 - 2 = 4.5 - 2 = 2.5$

4
- **a** $14 \div 2 = 7$
- **b** $46 \times 11 = 506$
- **c** $16 - 4 = 12$
- **d** $(106 + 5) \div 11 = 111 \div 11 \approx 10$
- **e** $6 \times 4 = 24$
- **f** $12^2 - 14 = 144 - 14 = 130$
- **g** $\dfrac{6 \times 6 + 3}{3 - 0.5} = \dfrac{39}{2.5} \approx \dfrac{40}{2.5} = 16$
- **h** $\left(\dfrac{9}{0.1}\right)^2 = 90^2 = 8100$
- **i** $3 \times 9^2 = 3 \times 81 \approx 3 \times 80 = 240$

5 Estimated cost of units = £0.25 × 100 = £25

VAT at 5% = £25 × $\dfrac{5}{100}$ = £$\dfrac{125}{100}$ = £1.25

Estimated bill ≈ £26

6 £400

7 3p

8 **a** 40 **b** 1.2 **c** 0.03 **d** 0.012

Ex BN3

1
- **a** £6
- **b** 22.5 m
- **c** 10 km
- **d** 40 g
- **e** £7.20
- **f** 16.8 km
- **g** £7.60
- **h** 4.02 m

2 **a** $\dfrac{1}{20}$ **b** $\dfrac{7}{40}$ **c** $\dfrac{1}{31}$ **d** $\dfrac{1}{20}$

3
- **a** $\dfrac{1}{2}$
- **b** $\dfrac{1}{16}$
- **c** 1
- **d** $\dfrac{1}{4}$
- **e** $\dfrac{7}{8}$
- **f** $\dfrac{13}{15}$
- **g** $3\dfrac{3}{5}$
- **h** $\dfrac{5}{14}$
- **i** $\dfrac{15}{44}$
- **j** $2\dfrac{1}{2}$
- **k** $2\dfrac{1}{2}$
- **l** $\dfrac{4}{25}$

4
- **a** 0.75
- **b** 0.4
- **c** 0.375
- **d** 0.56
- **e** 0.27
- **f** 0.15

5 **a** $\dfrac{1}{8}$ **b** 1 **c** you always get 1

6 $\dfrac{2}{9}$

7 C

8 Statement 1 is correct in actual £ and pence because £3.42 × 7 = £23.94 (whereas £3.43 × 7 = £24.01 which exceeds the weekly amount).
Statement 2 is *exact* because $\dfrac{£24}{7} = £3\dfrac{3}{7}$

Ex BN4

1 **a** $\dfrac{3}{10}$ **b** $\dfrac{3}{100}$ **c** $1\dfrac{27}{100}$ **d** $11\dfrac{9}{100}$ **e** $6\dfrac{101}{1000}$

2
- **a** $\dfrac{2}{5}$
- **b** $\dfrac{1}{20}$
- **c** $1\dfrac{1}{4}$
- **d** $11\dfrac{14}{25}$
- **e** $6\dfrac{1}{8}$
- **f** $12\dfrac{11}{20}$
- **g** $1\dfrac{81}{200}$
- **h** $6\dfrac{127}{250}$
- **i** $\dfrac{3}{200}$
- **j** $21\dfrac{3}{500}$

3
- **a** T, $\dfrac{111}{1000}$
- **b** R, 0.101101
- **c** R, 0.502777
- **d** T, $1\dfrac{1079}{5000}$

4 An exact price can only have two places after the decimal point to make whole cents. The nearest exact price is €9.67

5
- **a** 24.9
- **b** No. His check is only an estimate and is roughly correct

6
- **a** $\dfrac{5}{9}$
- **b** $\dfrac{7}{45}$
- **c** $\dfrac{2}{5}$
- **d** $\dfrac{19}{37}$
- **e** $1\dfrac{17}{30}$
- **f** $1\dfrac{5}{99}$
- **g** $2\dfrac{19}{90}$
- **h** $\dfrac{2}{75}$

7 **a** $0.\dot{5}$ **b** $0.\dot{1}4285\dot{7}$ **c** $0.0\dot{1}$ **d** $0.\dot{1}\dot{8}$

Ex BN5

1 **a** 6, 16, 45 **b** 18, 25, 90

2
- **a** $\dfrac{1}{3}$
- **b** $\dfrac{3}{5}$
- **c** $\dfrac{1}{12}$
- **d** $\dfrac{4}{7}$
- **e** $\dfrac{1}{2}$
- **f** $\dfrac{1}{4}$
- **g** $\dfrac{4}{9}$
- **h** $\dfrac{2}{3}$
- **i** $\dfrac{2}{5}$
- **j** $\dfrac{3}{10}$
- **k** $\dfrac{2}{5}$
- **l** $\dfrac{5}{12}$

3
- **a** 97.8, 100.9, 102
- **b** 0.219, 2.19, 21.9, 219
- **c** 0.1, 0.18, 0.29, 0.3
- **d** 6.04, 6.07, 6.17, 6.18
- **e** 8.9, 9, 9.1, 9.11
- **f** 3, 3.08, 3.79, 3.8

4
- **a** $\dfrac{1}{4}, \dfrac{1}{2}, \dfrac{3}{4}$
- **b** $\dfrac{5}{12}, \dfrac{2}{3}, \dfrac{5}{6}$
- **c** $\dfrac{3}{10}, \dfrac{13}{20}, \dfrac{4}{5}$
- **d** $\dfrac{1}{6}, \dfrac{7}{12}, \dfrac{3}{4}$
- **e** $\dfrac{2}{3}, \dfrac{13}{18}, \dfrac{7}{9}$
- **f** $\dfrac{1}{2}, \dfrac{3}{5}, \dfrac{13}{20}, \dfrac{7}{10}$

5 January

6 Second

7 **a** A $\dfrac{77}{200}$ B $\dfrac{23}{60}$ **b** B

Ex BN6

1
- **a** 0.35, 45%, $\dfrac{1}{2}$
- **b** 0.07, 70%, $\dfrac{4}{5}$
- **c** 69%, $\dfrac{3}{4}$, 80%
- **d** $\dfrac{2}{3}$, 68%, 0.7

2 0.52 (since $\dfrac{2}{5} = 0.4$)

3 $\dfrac{28}{40}$ = 70% so Celine has the best score

4 0.35 (as this is $\dfrac{35}{100}$)

5
- **a** 31.2 m
- **b** 22 men
- **c** £0.50
- **d** £7.20
- **e** 9.6 g
- **f** 78
- **g** 28 km
- **h** £462
- **i** 5.7 cm
- **j** £55
- **k** 5.4 m
- **l** 420

6 Definitely not – correct answer is £87.40

7 Ian by £2.50

8 $\dfrac{7}{8} = \dfrac{4}{8} + \dfrac{2}{8} + \dfrac{1}{8} + \dfrac{1}{2} + \dfrac{1}{4} + \dfrac{1}{8}$ = 50% + 25% + 12.5% = 87.5%

9

Fraction	Decimal	Percentage
$\dfrac{1}{100}$	0.01	1%
$\dfrac{7}{10}$	0.7	70%
$\dfrac{2}{5}$	0.4	40%

10 5%

Ex BN7

1   **a**   1   **b**   169   **c**   168

2   **a**   64   **b**   13   **c**   144   **d**   400
     e   13   **f**   0   **g**   133   **h**   10
     i   196   **j**   23

3   **a**   7   **b**   9   **c**   5   **d**   6
     e   11   **f**   12   **g**   3   **h**   2

4   **a**   20 cm   **b**   80 cm

5   120 cm

Ex BN8

1   **a** 2^6 **b** 3^3 **c** 5^5 **d** $2^2 \times 3^4$
     e $5^2 \times 6^4$ **f** $3^2 \times 10^3$

2   **a** $4 \times 4 \times 4$ **b** $5 \times 5 \times 5 \times 5$
     c $3 \times 3 \times 3 \times 2 \times 2 \times 2 \times 2 \times 2$
     d $4 \times 4 \times 4 \times 5 \times 5 \times 5$
     e $3 \times 3 \times 7 \times 7 \times 7 \times 7$

3   **a** $\frac{1}{1000}$ **b**   8000   **c**   1   **d** $\frac{2}{3}$ **e**   8
     f   2   **g**   2.01   **h**   4

4   **a** 2^9 **b** 5^9 **c** 4^9 **d** $3^{1.25}$ **e** $\left(\frac{1}{3}\right)^{\frac{5}{2}}$
     f 5^7 **g**   10   **h** $4^5 \times 3^6$ **i** $7^6 \times 4^3$ **j** $5^5 \times 3^3$
     k $5^6 \times 4$ **l** $6^7 \times 5$ **m** 2^5 **n** 4^2 **o** 7^5

5 0.5^4

6   9 or 81

7   **a** 2^{10} **b**   2, 4, 8, 16, 32, 64
     c   **i**   6   **ii**   14   **iii**   30
     d   It equals 2[last number − 1] = 2(512 − 1) = 1022
        Alternatively find 2 + 4 + 8 + 16 + 32 + 64 + 128
        + 256 + 512

Ex BN9

1   **a** $6\sqrt{3}$ **b** $60\sqrt{11}$ **c** $\sqrt{3}$ **d**   1
     e $3\sqrt{13}$ **f**   56   **g** $6\sqrt{15}$ **h**   64

2   **a** $5\sqrt{3}$ **b** $4\sqrt{3}$ **c** $15\sqrt{2}$ **d** $70\sqrt{2}$ **e** $6\sqrt{2}$

3   **a** $\sqrt{2}$ **b** $17\sqrt{3}$ **c**   24   **d** $20\sqrt{3}$

4   **a** $10 + 2\sqrt{5}$ **b** $6\sqrt{7} - 14$ **c**   40
     d $10 - \sqrt{2}$ **e** $38 + 12\sqrt{3}$ **f** $33 + 3\sqrt{7}$
     g $-12 + 3\sqrt{7}$ **h** $40 + 16\sqrt{5}$ **i** $17 - 2\sqrt{11}$

5   **a** $5 - 3\sqrt{5}$ **b** $-44 - 4\sqrt{5}$ **c** $24 + 8\sqrt{5}$
     d $6\sqrt{5} - 50$ **e** $-4 + 12\sqrt{5}$

6   **a** $10\sqrt{2}$ **b** $2\sqrt{10}$ **c** $\frac{5\sqrt{3}}{3}$
     d $\sqrt{6}$ **e** $\frac{\sqrt{10}}{5}$

7   **a** $\frac{6 - 2\sqrt{2}}{7}$ **b** $\frac{15 - 3\sqrt{5}}{20}$ **c** $9 + 3\sqrt{7}$

8   **a** g^2 **b** m^{-9} **c** $9r^4$ **d** $\frac{b^2}{2a^3}$

Ex BA1

1   Check graph is a straight line through the points
     (−4, −4) and (3, 10)

2   **a** $m = 6$ and $c = -2$ **b** $m = \frac{2}{3}$ and $c = 0$
     c $m = -1$ and $c = 8$

3   **a**   −3   **b** $y = -3x + 1$ **c** $y = -\frac{1}{3}x - 4$

4   −1

5   **a** $x = 0.4, y = 4.8$ **b** $x = 3.5, y = 3.3$
     c $x = -0.3, y = 1.3$

6 $x = 1.1, y = 3.3$

7 $k = -1$

8   No solutions as the lines are parallel

Ex BA2

1   **a**   **b**
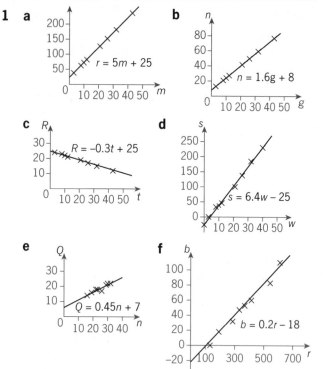
     c   **d**
     e   **f**

2   **a** $C = 15w + 30$
     b   Straight line graphs through the following points:
        Recipe book (0, 20) and (6, 140)
        Internet (0, 30) and (6, 120)
     c $w = 2$ pounds
     d $20w + 20 = 15w + 30$ so $5w = 10$ and $w = 2$

3   **a**
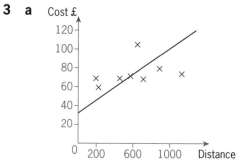
     b   Cost = 0.6 × distance + 36
     c   The scatter is so great that the line of best fit is not
        representative. Julia's idea is not a good one.

Ex BA3

1   **a** $x = 4, y = 7$ **b** $x = 6, y = -1$
     c $x = 4, y = 9$ **d** $c = 3, d = -1$
     e $x = 5, y = 4$ **f** $x = 2\frac{1}{2}, y = 7$
     g $x = \frac{1}{2}, y = -3$ **h** $p = 10, q = -1$
     i $x = 2, y = -7$ **j** $x = 8, y = -2$
     k $x = 2, y = 7$ **l** $x = 20, y = 3$
     m $l = \frac{1}{3}, m = -\frac{1}{2}$ **n** $x = \frac{4}{7}, y = -6\frac{5}{7}$
     o $g = 10, h = -5$

2   1 coffee costs £2.20 and 1 muffin costs £1.50

3   **a**   **i** $4p$ **ii**   c   **b** $4p + 2c = 208$
     c $p + c = 83, p = 21$ and $c = 62$, £1174

4   There are an infinite number of solutions (all points
     on the line), because the two graphs are the same
     straight line.

Ex BA4

1
a $x > 6$ **b** $x > 5$ **c** $x < 25$
d $y \leqslant 60$ **e** $x \geqslant 3.5$ **f** $p \leqslant 4.5$
g $d > 18$ **h** $f < 15$ **i** $r > 2\frac{1}{3}$
j $x \geqslant -1$ **k** $x < 1$ **l** $x \geqslant 10$
m $v \leqslant \frac{1}{2}$ **n** $c > 1\frac{1}{2}$ **o** $r < -6$
p $-\frac{1}{2} < x < 5$ **q** $-2 < x < 7$ **r** $7 \leqslant x \leqslant 11\frac{1}{2}$

2 **a**, **e**, **i**, **m**, **q**
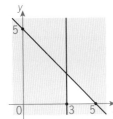

3 $3m + 7 \geqslant m + 25$ leading to $m \geqslant 9$
9 is the smallest possible number in a packet

4 **a** $x \leqslant 3$ **b** $y \geqslant 4$ **c** $x + y \leqslant 2$ **d** $y \geqslant x$

5 **a**, **b**, **c**, **d**, **e**, **f**, **g**, **h**

6 **a**, **b**
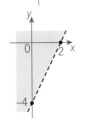

7 **a** Because the number of granary rolls bought is more than 2 × the number of white rolls bought. $w \geqslant 6$, $w + g < 20$

b
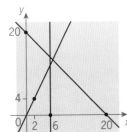
c £2.16

Only solution is $w = 6$, $g = 13$

Ex BG1

1 $a = 80°$ $b = 80°$ $c = 25°$ $d = 72°$
$e = 36°$ $f = 55°$ $g = 310°$ $h = 95°$
$i = 85°$ $j = 95°$ $x = 50°$

2 **a** 50°, 250° (since angles of a quadrilateral add to 360°)

b $49\frac{1}{11}°, 65\frac{5}{11}°, 65\frac{5}{11}°$ (since base angles of an isosceles triangle are equal and angle sum of a triangle is 180°)

3 $a + b + c = 180°$ (angles at a point). But the other two unmarked angles of the triangle are b and a (alternate angles). Therefore the angles of the triangle add to 180°.

4 **a** $c = a + b$ **b** $x = 24\frac{4}{9}°$

Ex BG2

1 **a** 101° **b** 90° **c** $a = 50°, b = 130°, c = 50°$
2 **a** 1080° **b** $x = 50°$
3 **a** Draw in a radius of the circle. Then using a protractor, draw a radius at intervals of 72°. This will give 5 points equally spaced on the circle. Join these 5 points.

b Draw in a radius of the circle. Then using a protractor, draw a radius at intervals of 60°. This will give 6 points equally spaced on the circle. Join these 6 points.

c Draw in a radius of the circle. Then using a protractor, draw a radius at intervals of $\frac{360°}{n}$. This will give n points equally spaced on the circle. Join these n points.

4 140°, 40°

5 **a** 3240° (can be divided into 18 triangles) 162° (i.e. 3240 ÷ 20)

b 20 × exterior angle = 360°, so exterior angle = 18°. Therefore, interior angle = 180° − 18° = 162°

6 Pentagons: No, because 360° is not divisible by the interior angle 108°
Hexagons: Yes, because 360° is divisible by the interior angle 120° so three hexagons can be fitted together at a point and leave no gaps.

7 $x = 180° - \frac{360°}{n}$ For a regular hexagon, this gives 180° − 60° = 120° (correct)

Ex BG3

1 **a** $x = 51°$ **b** $x = 126°, y = 124°$
c $x = 98°$ $y = 82°$ $z = 98°$
d $\alpha = 84°$ $\beta = 24°$
e $\alpha = 72°$ $\beta = 72°$ $\gamma = 144°$ **f** $\theta = 36°$

2 Assuming O is the centre of the circle,
$AOB = 180° - 2x$ $BAE = 90° - x$
$BDA = 90° - x$
This demonstrates the alternate segment theorem

3 $OQP = y$ (angles in the same segment) and therefore $OPQ = y$ (isosceles triangle).
Therefore AB is parallel to PQ by the reverse of the alternate angles theorem.

4 No, because angle SPQ is 100° not 90°

5 Various valid arguments

Ex BG4

1

1 , 2

2 Images will be triangles with vertices:
   a (2, 0), (0, −2), (3, −2)   **b** (2, 2), (3, 0), (0, 0)
   c (0, 2), (2, 3), (2, 0)

3

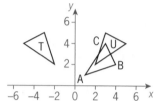

4 **a** reflection in the line $y = 5$
   b half-turn about (5, 4)

5 reflection in the line $x = 4$

6 **a** Q will have vertices (3, −1), (6, −1) and (4, −2)
   b R will have vertices (−1, 3), (−1, 6) and (−2, 4)
   c rotation of 90° about (0, 0)

7 **a** T will have vertices (−1, 2), (−1, 5) and (−3, 5)
   b U will have vertices (1, 2), (1, 5) and (3, 5)
   c reflection in the line $y = x$

Ex BG5

1 Translation $\begin{pmatrix} 4 \\ -3 \end{pmatrix}$, translation $\begin{pmatrix} -4 \\ 3 \end{pmatrix}$

2 **a** Translation $\begin{pmatrix} 6 \\ 0 \end{pmatrix}$ **b** Translation $\begin{pmatrix} 0 \\ -6 \end{pmatrix}$

3 **a** (−2, −3), (−4, −2) and (−1, −1)
   b (−2, 2), (−3, 0) and (−4, 3)

4 **a** $X'\,Y'Z'$ has vertices (0, −1), (−3, −3), (−1, 0)
   b $X''Y''Z''$ has vertices (−2, −1), (1, −3), (−1, 0)
   c reflection in the line $y = x + 3$

Ex BG6

1 $a = 9\,\text{cm}$ $b = 8\,\text{cm}$
2 **a** proof   **b** $x = 4.8$
3 $8.9\,\text{m}$
4 $4.8\,\text{cm}$
5 Proof
6 $\dfrac{x+6}{4} = \dfrac{6}{3}$
   Therefore $x = 2$

Ex BG7

1

2 Images will be pentagons with the following vertices:
   a (4, 2), (8, 2), (8, 4), (6, 4) and (4, 6)

   b $(4, 3\tfrac{1}{2})$, $(5, 3\tfrac{1}{2})$, $(5, 4)$, $(4\tfrac{1}{2}, 4)$ and $(4, 4\tfrac{1}{2})$

   c (−2, −1), (−4, −1), (−4, −2), (−3, −2) and (−2, −3)

3 **a**

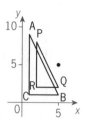

   b (5, 5)   **c** $\dfrac{3}{4}$

4 **a** Check graph
   b Check vertices of image are as listed below
   c A_1 (5, 2), B_1 (7, 4), C_1 (9, 0), D_1 (6, 0)

5 8

6 **a** yes – this is an enlargement sf 2
   b yes – this is an enlargement sf 1.25
   c no, because the ratio $\dfrac{15}{10} \neq$ the ratio $\dfrac{7.5}{6}$
   d yes – this is an enlargement sf 0.2. But this would make the original photograph smaller
   e yes – this is an enlargement sf 4.5
   f no, because the ratio $\dfrac{52.5}{15} \neq$ the ratio $\dfrac{33.5}{10}$

Ex BG8

1 **a** r **b** $2r$ **c** $-2p$ **d** $-q + r$ **e** $p + r$

2 **a** $b - a$ **b** $\tfrac{1}{2}(a + b)$ **c** $-\tfrac{1}{2}a$

   d $\tfrac{1}{2}(a - b)$ **e** $\tfrac{1}{2}b$

3 **a** $a + c$ **b** $c - a$ **c** $\tfrac{1}{2}a + c$

   d $a + \tfrac{4}{5}c$ **e** $\tfrac{1}{2}a - \tfrac{1}{5}c$

4 **a** $2p + 8q$
   b Yes. $\overrightarrow{OT} = 6p + 10q = \overrightarrow{OR} + p + 4q = \overrightarrow{OR}$

   $+ \tfrac{1}{2}\,\overrightarrow{PR}$ so T lies on line PR (N.B. can also

   use $\overrightarrow{OT} = \overrightarrow{OP} + 1\tfrac{1}{2}\,\overrightarrow{PR}$ to demonstrate this)

Ex BS1

1 **a** Weak negative correlation
   b Weak positive correlation
   c No correlation
   d Strong negative correlation

2 **a**

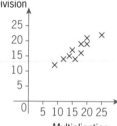

   b Strong positive correlation

   c

   d 21

e This score is outside the range of data plotted – the line of best fit may not be a good predictor for such a low score

3 a

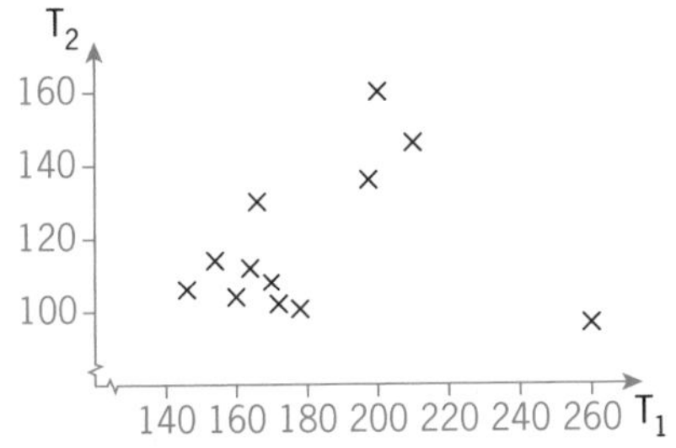

b There is very little evidence of correlation between the T_1 and T_2 times

c There is no suitable line of best fit so cannot estimate the T_2 time

4 a

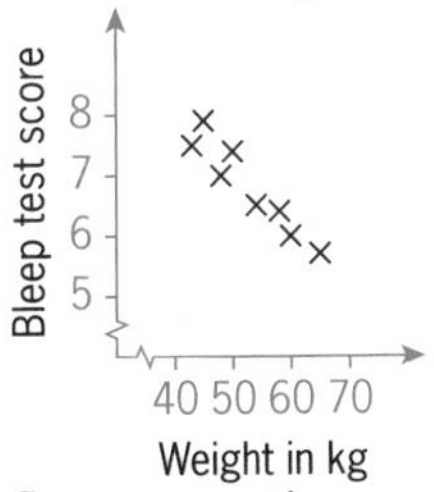

b Strong negative correlation

c

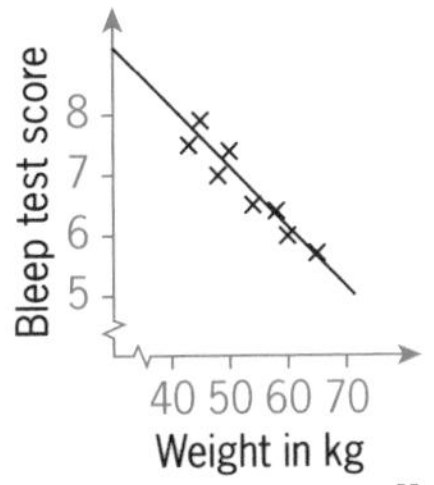

d i 53 kg   **ii** 7.0

Ex BS2

1 a

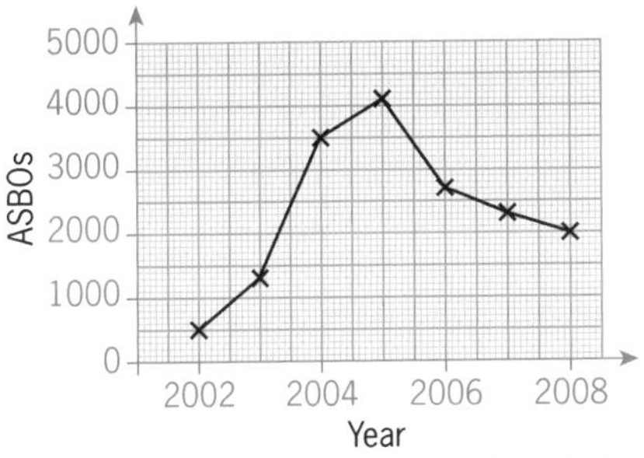

b The number of *ASBOs* rose sharply from 2002 to a maximum in 2005. They have subsequently fallen to half of the 2005 figure.

2 a Wed 12 pm

b 8 am Friday because the patient's temperature has settled at the normal of 36.9° by then

3 a

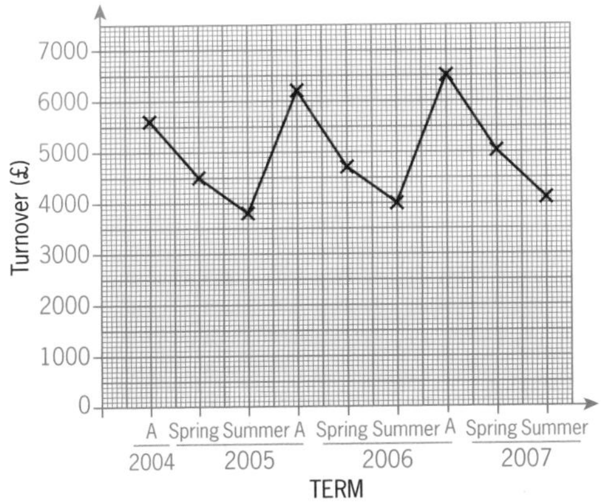

b The graph shows strong seasonal variation with turnover always being highest in the autumn term and lowest in the summer term. The overall trend in turnover is upward.

4 a

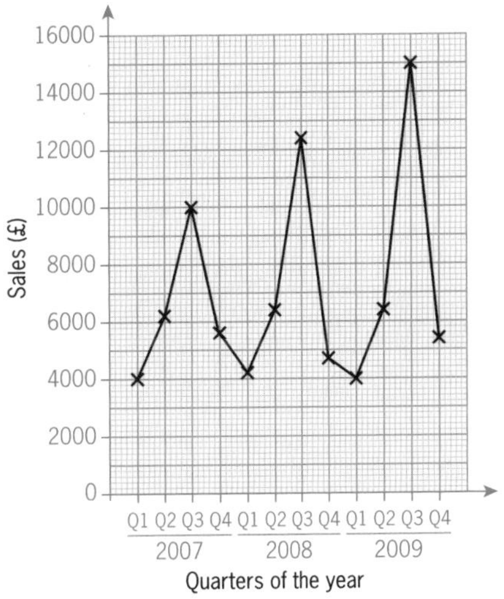

b As would be expected of a beach cafe, the graph shows strong seasonal variation with high sales peaks in the summer quarter. The overall trend in sales is upward.

c Winter 2008 as sales were much lower in $Q4$ 2008 than in the corresponding quarters of 2007 and 2009

Unit C

Ex CN1

1 $\frac{4}{15}$

2 a $\frac{1}{3}$ **b** £1584

3 a 4 days   **b** 25 m²   **c** $\frac{3}{5}$

4 a $\frac{4}{15}$ **b** $\frac{1}{15}$ **c** 3   **d** $\frac{19}{20}$

   e $\frac{11}{12}$ **f** $\frac{5}{9}$ **g** $\frac{8}{15}$ **h** $3\frac{1}{5}$

   i $4\frac{2}{5}$ **j** 11   **k** $2\frac{31}{35}$ **l** $1\frac{3}{7}$

5 He has multiplied the bottom of the fraction by 15 as well as the top. Correct answer is 10

6 Yes, but it can be expressed as $\frac{4}{5}$ by dividing top and bottom by 7

7 No – he will need 30

8 $19\frac{11}{20}$ m², $18\frac{3}{10}$ m

Ex CN2

1 a 7 complete jars

   b £1.56 (although he will only make a total of 7p profit at this price. Suggest he charges £1.70 per jar to ensure a total profit of over £1)

2 a 3   **b** 3.41   **c** 13   **d** 17 400

   e 0.0044   **f** 0.0000040

3 £6.02

4 2.55 kg and 2.45 kg

5 No. She could take as long as 12.5 secs for a length which would give 125 secs or 2 mins 5 secs for ten lengths. Bart might have only taken $1\frac{1}{2}$ mins for ten lengths.

6 a i 828.5 m   **ii** 828.25 m   **iii** 828.005 m
  b part **i**
7 £778.05 and £589.05
8 11.54°
9 23.34 km and 22.91 km

Ex CN3

1 a 0.563   **b** 3.62   **c** 1.07   **d** −0.0366
  e 3.86   **f** 8.39   **g** −85.9   **h** 0.829

2 47.8 cm² (3 sf)

3

x	−3	−2	−1	0	1
$5x^2 - x$	48	22	6	0	4

4 7.1 seconds
5 a 130.651   **b** $-\dfrac{5}{6} \approx -0.833$
  c 13.1 (3 sf)   **d** 25.4 cm³ (3 sf)
6 a £60   **b** £96   **c** 56 cm   **d** 76 m²
7 a 4.498   **b** 14.81   **c** 6.856   **d** −0.1611
8 £400 gives an increase of exactly 15%, so £399 is the most he could have paid

Ex CN4

1 a 4.792×10^2 **b** 3.829×10^{-3}
  c 1.25698×10^8 **d** -1.50348×10^2
  e 1.03259×10^{-3} **f** $6.85008600045 \times 10^{11}$
  g 8.70003×10^1 **h** 3.5097×10^0
2 a 26 700   **b** 314 000 000 000 000
  c 0.000 934   **d** 0.000 000 0108
  e 0.000 000 000 12   **f** 207 000 000
  g 661 900   **h** 0.000 000 000 002 016
3 The following answers are rounded to 3 sf where that seems sensible.
  a 1.5785×10^{12} **b** 5.97×10^6
  c 3.10×10^{12} **d** 8.37×10^3
  e 2.00×10^{15} **f** 2.16×10^{10}
  g 2.27×10^3 **h** 1.92×10^{-17}
  i 4.32×10^5 **j** 6.90×10^{15}
4 a 1.083×10^{12} km³   **b** 5.958×10^{21} tonnes
5 From 7×10^{17} m to 3.5×10^{18} m
6 a 97 200 tonnes   **b** 9000
7 a 7.87×10^{13} m³   **b** 8.069×10^{16} kg (4 sf)

Ex CN5

1 a £6.15   **b** 2.94 km   **c** 1.32 kg
  d 8.715 m   **e** 1.8 hrs
  f 0.46p (sensible answer is 0p, i.e. nothing)
2 168 cm²
3 37.5%
4 a £1564 to nearest £
  b £1298 to nearest £
5 a 6 kg   **b** 106 kg (nearest kg)
  c As he puts on weight and passes age 30, the increase per year is likely to level off
6 £6450 (3 sf)
7 a 396 cm²   **b** 88%   **c** 12%
8 a £273 000 (3 sf)
  b It is unlikely that house prices will rise by the same percentage for such a long period
  c 2086

9 After 5 years, the bond gives a total of £3286.85 whereas the savings account gives £3250. Obviously, the bond is the better investment if Joan can afford to leave her money untouched for 5 years. If she is likely to need access to some of it within the 5 year period, then she should go for the savings account.
10 £16 415

Ex CN6

1 25 km
2 No – she has only eaten 1081.25 kcal
3 a 287.5 g of butter, 175 g of castor sugar, 5 eggs, 537.5 g plain flour
  b Because the recipe needs exactly 1 egg for every 5 muffins
4 15 hours
5 $b = 70$
6 $b = 8$
7 a $p = 0.625$ **b** $q = 0.791$
8 a $p = 25\sqrt{2} \approx 35.4$ **b** $q = 32$
9 a $l = \dfrac{12}{d^2}$ **b** 0.03 lux
10 $3\frac{1}{2}$ hours

Ex CN7

1 20 km/hr
2 95 km
3 40 mins
4 a 19 cm³   (2 sf)
  b £8.81 assuming there is no charge for the manufacture of the bracelet
5 ● Anyone who sends less than 25 text messages per month
  ● Anyone who sends more than 25 text messages per month
6 0.5 miles
7 56 000 square miles
8 Large house £27   Small house £9
9 80 mins = 1 hr 20 mins
10 a 145 cm³   **b** 375 cm³   **c** $1\frac{1}{3}$ mins

Ex CN8

1 £13 530.56
2 No – he will only get back approximately £33 874
3 a i 500 000
    ii there were 500 000 bacteria to start with
  b 488   **c** 19 hours
4 a −1.59   **b** $0.5^{-1.59} = 3.010\ldots$
5 8.75 mg
6 a $0.99956^{1500} \approx 0.5168$ and $0.99956^{1600} \approx 0.4945$. Therefore the half life lies between 1500 and 1600 years
  b 1575 years
7 1.38×10^{19}
8 a 25 745 000   **b** 33 644 000

Ex CA1

1 a (0, 0, 5)   **b** (−3, 2, −1)
  c (0, 5, 0)   **d** (−3, 4, −2)
  e (3.5, 4, −18)   **f** (−2.5, 1.25, 2.5)

Ex CA2

1 **a** 2.6 **b** 1.9 **c** 3.0
   d 3.5 **e** 1.9 **f** −0.2
2 **a** 2.63 **b** 1.86 **c** −1.06
3 **a** Need to solve $w(w + 1)(w + 2) = 100$
     At $w = 3$, $w(w + 1)(w + 2) = 60$ (smaller than 100)
     and at $w = 4$, $w(w + 1)(w + 2) = 120$ (larger than
     100). Therefore solution lies between $w = 3$ and
     $w = 4$ i.e. $3 < w < 4$
   b 3.713

Ex CA3

1 **a** $x^2 + 11x + 24$ **b** $x^2 − 3x − 54$
   c $x^2 + 9x − 10$ **d** $x^2 − 12x + 35$
   e $x^2 + 14x + 49$ **f** $x^2 − 8x + 16$
   g $2x^2 + 5x + 3$ **h** $6x^2 − 8x − 8$
   i $4x^2 + 23x − 35$ **j** $15x^2 − 41x + 14$
   h $4x^2 + 20x + 25$ **l** $9x^2 − 24x + 16$
2 **a** $2x^2 − 3x − 20$ **b** $2x^2 − 16x + 22$
   c $5x$
3 **a** $(x + 5)(x + 4)$ **b** $(x + 7)(x + 3)$
   c $(x + 6)(x + 1)$ **d** $(x + 9)(x + 5)$
   e $(x − 8)(x + 5)$ **f** $(x − 7)(x + 2)$
   g $(x − 11)(x + 3)$ **h** $(x − 7)(x + 6)$
   i $(x + 10)(x − 8)$ **j** $(x + 6)(x − 2)$
   k $(x + 12)(x − 6)$ **l** $(x + 9)(x − 8)$
   m $(x − 1)(x − 1)$ **n** $(x − 6)(x − 4)$
   o $(x − 5)(x − 4)$ **p** $(x − 12)(x − 8)$
4 **a** $2(x + 2)(x + 3)$ **b** $3(x + 2)(x + 1)$
   c $(x − 9)(x + 9)$ **d** $(x − 12)(x + 12)$
   e $x(x − 9)$ **f** $4(x − 9)(x + 2)$
   g $(x − \frac{1}{2})(x + \frac{1}{2})$ **h** $x(x + 12)$
   i $(2x − 3)(2x + 3)$ **j** $x^2(x − 3)$
   k $(3x − \frac{4}{7})(3x + \frac{4}{7})$ **l** $7(x − 2)(x + 2)$
5 **a** $(2x + 1)(x + 4)$ **b** $(3x + 2)(2x + 1)$
   c $(4x − 3)(2x + 3)$ **d** $(5x + 3)(x − 4)$
   e $(6x − 5)(x − 8)$ **f** $(4x − 3)(3x + 2)$
   g $x(x + 9)(x + 2)$ **h** $x(x − 8)(x + 7)$
   i $2x(x − 3)(x + 3)$ **j** $5\left(x − \frac{1}{6}\right)\left(x + \frac{1}{6}\right)$
   k $x^2(x − 3)^2$ **l** $3x^2(x − 9)(x + 9)$
6 $4x^2 + 11x − 14$

Ex CA4

1 **a** $2a$ **b** $\dfrac{6u}{w}$ **c** $\dfrac{7}{h^3}$ **d** $\dfrac{2m}{n}$
   e $\dfrac{2c^5}{3d^5e^2}$ **f** $\dfrac{3r^4}{4t^3}$ **g** $\dfrac{3}{ab}$ **h** $3x^2y$
2 **a** $\dfrac{1}{5}$ **b** $\dfrac{4}{7}$ **c** $\dfrac{3}{x + 4}$ **d** $\dfrac{x + 4}{3}$
   e $\dfrac{x + 4}{x − 3}$ **f** $\dfrac{x − 3}{x − 4}$ **g** $\dfrac{2x + 3}{2}$ **h** $\dfrac{2x − 1}{x − 5}$
   i $\dfrac{2x + 5}{4x + 1}$ **j** $\dfrac{x}{6x + 1}$
3 $\dfrac{x + 3}{4x + 1}$

4 **a** 3 **b** $\dfrac{12a}{7}$ **c** $\dfrac{n}{m}$ **d** $\dfrac{15}{g^2}$
   e $\dfrac{8}{3}$ **f** $\dfrac{f}{2p^2}$ **g** $\dfrac{5}{y}$ **h** $\dfrac{2(x − 9)(x − 2)}{x^2 − 17x + 18}$
5 $\dfrac{x − 2}{8} \times \dfrac{7}{x^2 − 4} = \dfrac{1}{4}$
   Solution is $x = 5\frac{1}{2}$, so dimensions are
   $\dfrac{15}{16}$ by $\dfrac{28}{105}$

Ex CA5

1 **a** −4, −3 **b** −3, −8 **c** −2, 7
   d −8, 9 **e** −7, 4 **f** −10, 2
   g 4, 6 **h** 5, 6 **i** 0, 8
   j −2, 0 **k** −4, 4 **l** −4
2 **a** $−2, −\dfrac{1}{2}$ **b** $\dfrac{2}{−3}, 3$ **c** $−\dfrac{1}{2}, −\dfrac{1}{3}$
   d $−5, \dfrac{1}{4}$ **e** $\dfrac{2}{5}, −1\dfrac{1}{2}$ **f** $\dfrac{3}{4}, 1\dfrac{1}{3}$
   g $\dfrac{1}{±3}$ **h** $−1\dfrac{1}{2}$
3 **a** $(x + 5)^2 − 13$ **b** $(x + 2)^2 + 3$
   c $(x − 6)^2 − 33$ **d** $(x + 1)^2 + 10$
   e $(x + 3)^2 − 11$ **f** $(x + 10)^2 − 116$
   g $(x − 7)^2 − 49$ **h** $(x − 9)^2 − 100$
4 **a** $−4 ± \sqrt{23}$ **b** $−3 ± \sqrt{7}$
   c $−1 ± \sqrt{3}$ **d** $−6 ± \sqrt{29}$
   e $2 ± \sqrt{10}$ **f** $3 ± \sqrt{10}$
   g $5 ± \sqrt{14}$ **h** $8 ± \sqrt{2}$
5 **a** 5.85, −0.854 **b** 0.162, −6.16
   c −4, 0.5 **d** $2, −\dfrac{1}{2}$
   e 2.26, 0.591 **f** 0.545, −2.29
   g 1, 0.6 **h** 3.90, −0.898
6 **a** $x = 3.419$ **b** perimeter = 2(10.419 +
     3.838) = 28.5 cm (3 sf)
7 Solution is $x = −2 ± \sqrt{\dfrac{11}{2}} = −2 ± \sqrt{\dfrac{22}{2}}$

Ex CA6

1 **a** U-shaped parabola with minimum at
     (0, −2) cutting x-axis at (−1.4, 0) and (1.4, 0)
   b U-shaped parabola with minimum at (0, 3)
   c U-shaped parabola with minimum at (0, −5) cutting
     x-axis at (−2.2, 0) and (2.2, 0)
   d U-shaped parabola with minimum at (0, −1) cutting
     x-axis at (−0.7, 0) and (0.7, 0)
   e U-shaped parabola with minimum at
     (0, −3) cutting x-axis at (−1.2, 0) and (1.2, 0)
   f U-shaped parabola with minimum at (0, −7)
     cutting x-axis at (−3.2, 0) and (3.2, 0)
   g Dome shaped parabola with maximum at (0, 10)
     cutting x-axis at (±3.2, 0)
   h Dome shaped parabola with maximum at (0, 2)
     cutting x-axis at (±1.4, 0)
2 **a** ±1.4 **b** ±2.2 **c** ±3.2
   d ±0.7 **e** ±3 **f** ±1.3
   g ±2 **h** ±2.2
3 **a** $x = ±1.2$ **b** $x = ±1.3$ **c** $x = ±2.4$
   d $x = ±1.4$ **e** 0 **f** No solutions
4 $k < −6$
5 **a** U-shaped parabola with minimum at (1, −4) cutting
     x-axis at (−1, 0) and (3, 0) and y-axis at (0, −3)

b *U*-shaped parabola with minimum at $(\frac{1}{2}, -4\frac{1}{4})$ cutting *x*-axis at (−1.6, 0) and (2.6, 0) and *y*-axis at (0, −4)

c *U*-shaped parabola with minimum at (2, 3) cutting *y*-axis at (0, 7)

d *U*-shaped parabola with minimum at (0.75, 3.9) cutting *y*-axis at (0, 5)

e *U*-shaped parabola with minimum at (−0.2, −1.1) cutting *x*-axis at (0.4, 0) and (−0.8, 0) and *y*-axis at (0, −1)

f Dome shaped parabola with maximum at (1.5, 11.5) cutting *x*-axis at (−0.9, 0) and (3.9, 0) and *y*-axis at (0, 7)

6 **a** 3.5, −1.5　**b** −1.6, 2.6　**c** 0.6, 3.4
　d −1, 2.5　**e** −1.6, 1.3　**f** 0.4, 2.6

7 **a** $V = 3x^2 - 6x$

b *U*-shaped parabola through (0, 0), (1, −1), (2, 0), (3, 9), (4, 24)

c To ensure the volume is positive

d $x = 3.8$

Ex CA7

All solutions are given as a point pair (*x*, *y*)

1 **a** (−2, 0), (3, 0)　**b** (−2, 0), (1, 0)
　c (−2, 0), (2, 0)　**d** (−4.6, 11.8), (3.1, 7.9) (1dp)
　e $(-1\frac{1}{2}, 9)$, (2, 2)　**f** $\left(-1\frac{1}{9}, 2\frac{1}{9}\right)$, (1,3)

2 **a** (−2.7, 1.7), (0.7, −1.7)
　b (−11.2, −3.2), (−5.8, 2.2)
　c (3.1, 1.8), (5.4, −2.8)
　d (0.8, 0.6), (1.5, −1.6)
　e No solutions　**f** (−0.2, 2.3), (1.8, 5.1)

3 **a** (1.3, 1.6), (−0.8, −2.6)
　b (1.8, 5.6), (−2.8, 9.5)　**c** (2.9, 4.7)

4 $P = (-6, 5)$ $Q = (-2\frac{1}{4}, -2\frac{1}{2})$ $PQ = 8.4$ (1dp)

Ex CA8

1 **a**

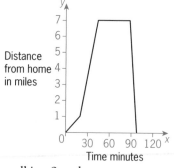

b walking 3 mph
bus 24mph
car 42 mph

c steeper gradient shows an increased speed on the bus

d • Suggests uniform speed
• Suggests the only waiting time is before his lesson

2 **a**

x	0	1	2	3	4	5
y	0	16	24	24	16	0

b The graph is a dome shaped parabola with a maximum point at $(2\frac{1}{2}, 25)$ and passing through (0, 0) and (5, 0)

c **i** 25 m　**ii** 0.7 secs and 4.3 secs　**iii** 3.2 secs

3 **a** 40 cm　　**b** $L = \dfrac{1000}{s^2}$

c The graph will be a curve through the points

s	5	10	15	20	25	30
L	40	10	4.4	2.5	1.6	1.1

Ex CA9

1 **a**
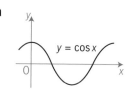

b
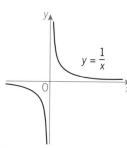

c
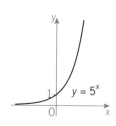

d
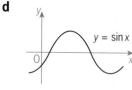

e
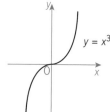

2 **a**
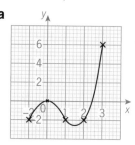

b
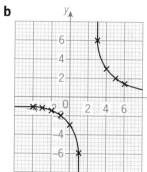

c
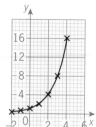

d
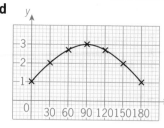

3 **a**
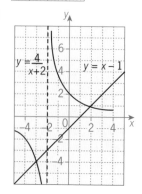

b $x = -2$ because it gives division by zero

c $x = 2$, $y = 1$ and $x = -3$, $y = -4$

d   Because we need to solve $\dfrac{4}{x+2} = x - 1$

which gives $4 = (x - 1)(x + 2)$. This gives $x^2 + x - 2 = 4$ which leads to $x^2 + x - 6 = 0$

4   **a**   C   **b**   B

     c   D   **d**   A

Ex CA10

1   **a** $y = 1.25 (1 + \sin x)$ **b** $y = \sin(x + 30°)$

     c $y = 2\cos x$ **d** $y = x^2 - 3$

     e $y = (x + 1)^2$ **f** $y = -x^2$

2   **a**   (6, 8)   **b**   (6, 20)   **c**   (13, 4)

     d   (6, −4)   **e**   (1, 4)   **f**   (6, 2)

     g   (6, 3)   **h** $(1\frac{1}{3}, 6)$ **i**   (−6, 4)

3   **a**   **b**

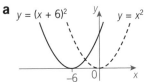

     c

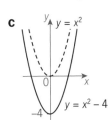

4 $t = 30°$

Ex CG1

1   **a**   64 m²   **b**   74 m²

     c   104 units²   **d**   74 units²

2 $x = 22$ Area = 294 units²

3   **a**   9312 m²   **b**   £5504

4   Many answers possible

5   Trapezium = lower triangle + upper triangle

$= \frac{1}{2} ah + \frac{1}{2} bh = \frac{1}{2} (a+b)h$

6   £96.32

Ex CG2

1   **a**   36π m², 12 π m   **b**   113 m², 37.7 m

2   **a**   251.3 cm   **b**   50 265 m

     c   40 (39 complete turns)

3   **a**   94.2 m   **b**   644 m²

4   **a**   18.3 m   **b**   137.4 m²   **c**   48.3 m

5   144°   **6**   0.19 cm²

7   12.5 cm²   **8**   12.3 m

Ex CG3

1   **a**   **i**   36 cm³   **ii**   1445 m³   **iii**   848 m³ (nearest m³)

     b   519 m² (nearest m²)

2   **a** $V = \frac{1125}{2} \pi \approx 1767$ units³

          SA $= 225\pi \approx 706.9$ units²

     b $V = 100\pi \approx 314.2$ m³

          SA $= 90\pi \approx 282.7$ m²

3   100.7 cm²   **4**   0.24 cm   **5** $\frac{2}{3}$

Ex CG4

1   **a**   4   **b**   16   **c**   192 cm²

     d   64   **e**   5.34 cm³

2   5.6 litres

3 $533\frac{1}{3}$ cm²

4   **a**   144 cm²   **b**   2304 cm³

5   **a**   400 mm²   **b**   9000 mm³   **c**   120 cm²

     d   5 000 000 m²   **e**   73 000 cm²

     f   3.2 m³   **g**   435 km²

6   53.125 cm³

7   20 000 cm²

Ex CG5

1   **a** $YZ = 3.32$

     b $\overrightarrow{ACB} = 37.5°$

     c $PR = 10.01$

     d $\overrightarrow{EFB} = 76.6°$

2   33.0 m

3   16.2 km

4   12.6 cm

5   Area $= \frac{1}{2} bh$ and $h = a\sin C$ so Area $= \frac{1}{2} ab \sin C$

as required

Area $= 21.2$ m²

6   51.4°

Ex CG6

1   **a**   11.7 m   **b**   19 m   **c**   52.1°

2   **a**   13.1 m   **b**   44.4°

3   **a**   14.1 cm   **b**   17.3 cm   **c**   45°

4   **a**   201.2 m   **b**   203.5 m   **c**   8.5°

5   **a**   23.1°   **b**   25.7°   **c**   65.3°

Ex CS1

1 $\frac{1}{6}$

2   **a**   Because only one of the 6 sections is coloured purple

     b   **i** $\frac{2}{3}$ **ii** $\frac{1}{3}$ **iii** $\frac{2}{3}$

3   **a** $\frac{4}{9}$ **b**   4   **c**   4

4   48

5   **a** $p(\text{lime}) = \frac{15}{100} = \frac{3}{20}$. If there are 8 lime

sweets and N is the number of sweets,

then $\frac{8}{N} = \frac{3}{20}$ giving $N = \frac{160}{3}$ which is not

a whole number (impossible).

     b   200

     c   0.2

     d   Strawberry 4, Orange 8, Lime 3, Blackcurrant 5

6   **a**   3 times as many   **b**   0.36

Ex CS2

1   2358, 2385, 2538, 2583, 2853, 2835

3258, 3285, 3528, 3582, 3825, 3852

5238, 5283, 5328, 5382, 5823, 5832

8235, 8253, 8325, 8352, 8523, 8532

2   **a**

		Peter		
		Red	Purple	Green
Jack	Purple	PR	PP	PG
	Orange	OR	OP	OG

     b $\frac{1}{6}$

3 0.6

4 a

	1	3	5
1	2	4	6
2	3	5	7
4	5	7	9

b i $\frac{1}{9}$ **ii** $\frac{2}{9}$ **iii** $\frac{4}{9}$

5 $\frac{21}{36} = \frac{7}{12}$

6 a i 0.025 **ii** 0.231
  b i the ratio of men to women teachers
   ii 60s because it is 12% for both men and women

EX CS3

1 Red 1 section
  Green 3 sections
  Orange 1 section
  Yellow 1 section
  Blue 4 sections

2 a Gary as he has carried out by far the most trials
  b 509
  c Altogether there are 1010 trials, so if coin unbiased would expect approx 505 heads and 505 tails. We have 501 heads and 509 tails which is very close to the expected figures and therefore suggests the coin is unbiased

3 a

Score	Frequency
1	3
2	3
3	4
4	3
5	4
6	3
Total	**20**

If unbiased, would expect $3\frac{1}{3}$ occurrences of each number, i.e. 3 of some and 4 of others. Results therefore suggest coin unbiased (but based on only 20 trials this conclusion is unreliable)

  b $\frac{1}{5}$

4 a Greg, computer, computer
  b Yes. He is moving towards a probability of 0.6 of winning, whereas he had lost 3 of the first 4 games.
  c 0.6

5 a

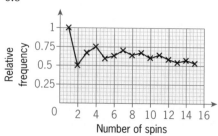

  b 3
  c No. There may be a section with another colour (prob 0.2). Would have expected 3 occurrences but this is not certain to happen.

EX CS4

1 a

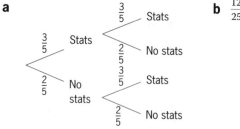

  b i 0.0025 **ii** 0.095

2 a

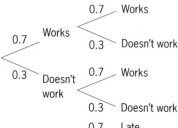

  b $\frac{12}{25}$

3 a 1st detector 2nd detector **b** 0.09

4 a **b** 0.38

5 a

  b i $\frac{7}{20}$ **ii** $\frac{1}{2}$

6 a

  b $\frac{1}{2}$ **c** $\frac{1}{2}$

Practice papers

Full answers to the practice papers are on the enclosed CD-ROM